Juicing for Life

by Beverley Ramages

Copyright © 2016 Stanborough Press Ltd
First printed 2016 and reprinted 2016.

British Library Cataloguing in Publication Data. A catalogue record for this book is available from the British Library.

ISBN: 978-1-909545-88-5

Published by the Stanborough Press Ltd, Alma Park, Grantham, Lincolnshire, UK.

Edited by Julian Hibbert
Nutritional adviser: Jennifer Holden, BSc, RD
Designed by David Bell

Printed in China.

Readers are hereby advised that the information contained in this recipe book should in no way be construed as a substitute for sound medical guidance, or as advice to dramatically alter their diet or relinquish necessary medications. Always consult with your regular medical practitioner before taking any such steps. Neither the author nor the publishers will be held responsible for any resulting ill effects.

The pictures used in this book are for illustrative purposes only, and may not fully represent the finished product of any recipe contained herein.

Contents

Tables of measurements
Any discrepancies due to rounding (to 3 significant figures)

Metric		Imperial
1 centimetre (cm)	=	0.394 inches
10 millilitres (ml)	=	0.352 fluid ounces
100 grams (g)	=	3.53 ounces

Imperial		Metric
1 inch (")	=	2.54 centimetres
1 fluid ounce (fl oz)	=	28.4 millilitres
1 ounce (oz)	=	28.3 grams

Culinary Conversion

Culinary*		Millilitres	Fluid Ounces
1 teaspoon (tsp)	=	5.92	0.208
1 tablespoon (tbsp)	=	17.8	0.625
1 cup (c)	=	237	8.33

Food Energy Equivalents

10 food calories (kcal)	=	41.8 kilojoules
1 kilojoule (kJ)	=	0.239 food calories

*Culinary measurements may vary, but amounts given here are internationally standardised units of measurement for juicing, cooking and baking.

Sources
Except where otherwise indicated, the information given in this book has been drawn from the following sources:

• Brendan McCarthy, *The Jumpstart 7 Day Weight Loss Program*, Creative Nations International Ltd, 2006
• Shelly Null and Gary Null, PhD, *The Joy of Juicing*
• Cherie Calbom, MS, CN, *Weekend Weight-loss Diet*
• Dr Ernst Schneider, *Healthy by Nature*, volume 1, Editorial Safeliz, 2006
• *www.Bembu.com* – '20 Diuretic Foods to Lower Blood Pressure and Lose Weight'
• *www.whfoods.com* – various articles on the benefits and nutritional value of various vegetables and fruits
• *www.medicalnewstoday.com/articles/265990.php* – article *270435.php*; article *276903.php*
• George D. Pamplona-Roger, MD, *Healthy Foods*, Editorial Safeliz, 2007
• *www.organicfacts.net* – 'Health Benefits of Lemon'
• *www.thebestofrawfood.com/benefits-of-beet-juice.html*
• *www.webmd.com/vitamins-and-supplements/lifestyle-guide-11/iron-supplements*
• *www.globalhealingcenter.com/natural-health/benefits-of-cayenne-pepper*
• *www.flatulencecures.com/effects-of-peppermint-tea*
• *www.organicfacts.net/health-benefits/herbs-and-spices/health-benefits-of-coriander.html*
• *www.organicfacts.net/health-benefits/herbs-and-spices/health-benefits-of-lemongrass.html*

Foreword

by Sharon Platt-McDonald, MSc, RM, RHV, RGN

W hy juice when you could eat the whole fruit with the added benefits of its fibre? Perhaps the answer lies in knowing when it may be helpful to include juice as part of the diet, with a clear understanding of the dietary requirements and cautions associated with some health conditions – something the author strives to do.

In *Juicing for Life* Beverley Ramages provides an argument based on her own personal health journey, the experiences of others and research. However, she realises that the consumption of whole fruits and vegetables is generally preferable to juicing it: 'I do not believe that humans were created to live on juice alone. We have teeth, jaws, salivary glands and a digestive system that ought to be used for the purpose for which they were created, for chewing, biting, masticating and digesting. Our systems are designed to digest whole foods.'

Keeping this in mind she states that, 'although juices can be adapted and used by almost anyone, they should not be used as a substitute for whole foods.'

Apart from the attractive and vibrant appearance of this publication, it comes with a wealth of nutritional information on the ingredients; practical tips on their other uses, such as cleaning agents and cosmetics; and information about the preparation, storage and preservation of food items.

It is important, however, to bear in mind the health concerns around injudicious juicing: the lack of fibre; high sugar content (from fruits) for diabetics; goitrogens[1] (in large amounts of raw vegetables) and their impact on the thyroid; oxalic acid and kidney health; and sorbitol (natural fruit sugar) and stomach upsets.[2]

From a dental perspective it is important to remember this advice from Dr Uchenna Okoye: 'Juice from fruits has a high acid content and can damage the enamel of your teeth in exactly the same way that a fizzy drink does. . . . If you're going to drink juices, always use a straw. Never brush your teeth straight after drinking, as the teeth are weakened by the exposure to acid.'[3]

Considering juicing? This is good advice from the Mayo Clinic: 'If you don't enjoy eating fresh fruits and vegetables, juicing may be a fun way to add them to your diet or to try fruits and vegetables you normally wouldn't eat. . . . If you do try juicing, make only as much juice as you can drink at one time because fresh squeezed juice can quickly develop harmful bacteria. And when juicing, try to keep some of the pulp. Not only does it have healthy fibre, but it can help fill you up.'[4]

It is good to see the author's emphasis on the need for balance: 'For juicing to have a positive lasting effect on our health or weight, it should be combined with other lifestyle changes like adequate sleep, vigorous exercise, proper nutrition, and the drinking of enough water daily. . . .'

Why not buy the book, enjoy the recipes and see the results for yourself.

Sharon

---

[1]Goitrogens: substances that disrupt the production of thyroid hormones by interfering with iodine uptake in the thyroid gland
[2]http://bestforjuicing.com/is-juicing-dangerous-or-safe/ [3]http://www.dailymail.co.uk/health/article-2912353/Is-juicing-making-fat-Not-mention-rotting-teeth-starving-body-nutrients-new-fad-not-healthy-all.html#ixzz3xsSI1C1V [4]http://www.mayoclinic.org/healthy-lifestyle/nutrition-and-healthy-eating/expert-answers/juicing/faq-20058020

Juicing Basics

Can I juice?

People juice for various reasons. There are many juicing books that have been written by people who started juicing either for their general health or specifically for weight loss. These books are inspirational because they are based on someone's story about how juicing has actually worked for them. I started juicing a couple of years ago. It began as a lifestyle experiment. I have a rather sedentary lifestyle and I wanted to see whether I could actually skip a meal and not feel hungry. Once my mind and stomach adjusted to missing a meal I began to notice that I was experiencing other benefits. My hair was glossier, my skin was more radiant, my eyesight improved, I had lots of energy; I lost weight and kept it off, my overall health improved and my sugar cravings all but disappeared. I was intrigued.

But as I shared my story with others, I discovered a whole world of juicing folk out there. It was exciting! I was not alone! There were others to whom juicing was just normal. I am a creationist, however, and I do not believe that humans were created to live on juice alone. We have teeth, jaws, salivary glands and a digestive system that ought to be used for the purpose for which they were created, for chewing, biting, masticating and digesting. Our systems are designed to digest whole foods.

So although juices can be adapted and used by almost anyone, they should not be used as a substitute for whole foods. For juicing to have a positive lasting effect on our health or weight, it should be combined with other lifestyle changes like adequate sleep, vigorous exercise, proper nutrition, and the drinking of enough water daily, among other things.

Juicing and smoothies are a great way to get kids, invalids and the aged to have their daily quota of nutrients. You can serve these drinks straight from the juicer or blender, with ice or mixed with crushed ice as a slush.

What really confirmed me as a juicer was the discovery of fresh juice as a healing food. My son, who was busy with his PhD at the time, gave me such great reviews and became such an enthusiastic participant in my experiment that I started paying more attention to what he was saying. I realised that there was much more to juicing than just weight loss or physical healing. From my personal experience and research, just one portion of juice a day can have a host of benefits:

- Slowing down the ageing process
- Enhancing skin and hair condition
- Detoxification of the system
- Increasing energy levels
- Appetite rejuvenation/improved taste sensation
- Ensuring adequate nutrition
- Helping to restore flagging health
- Fostering mental alertness
- Relief of menopause symptoms
- Weight control – maintaining, gaining or losing
- Helping to reduce the risk of osteoporosis
- Assisting in the curbing of stress
- Bringing the zest back into life

There are no long-term benefits in juicing sporadically. For maximum benefit in any of the areas mentioned above you should aim for at least one juice a day, preferably a green juice.

Tools

The two basic tools that you will need for a convenient and enjoyable juicing and smoothie experience are a good juicer and an equally capable blender. There are three main types of juicing machine on the market: centrifugal, masticating (single-gear juicers) and triturating juicers (twin-gear juicers). Each one has its pros and cons.

Centrifugal juicing machines – These are probably the most common and certainly the most affordable of the juicers. These are usually upright devices with a large chute and they are easy to clean. If you are just beginning to juice, are on a tight budget, or are not sure whether you are going to be a serious juicer, I'd recommend a centrifugal-type juicer. They are fast but their high speed (rpm) generates more heat, which in turn causes oxidation. In practical terms, this means that you should drink your juice almost immediately after it has been processed.

Handy tip: Roll up your leafy vegetables for easier juice extraction when using this kind of appliance.

Masticating (single-gear) juicing machines –
This type of machine will juice just about any type of fruit and vegetable, including leafy vegetables. It is generally accepted that they extract more juice than a centrifugal-type juicer. They are more expensive, however; take longer to reduce the ingredients to juice; and require more effort to clean.

Triturating juicing machines –
These appliances are generally considered to be the crème de la crème of juicers. They produce the best-quality juice because they operate at a lower speed and use dual gears that help to maximise both the quality and the quantity of juice produced. They are generally slower than the centrifugal juicers and are usually the most expensive ones to buy.

If you are just beginning to juice, or if you know that you will just be a casual juicer, then go for what you can afford – a centrifugal juicer will be fine. On the other hand, if juicing is going to be a part of your daily routine then you would be wise to spend some time trying to understand why there are different types of machines, what makes them different and which one would suit your needs over the long term.

The main difference between a juicer and a blender is that a juicer *removes the juice* from the fruit or vegetable, leaving the pulp, which contains fibre (this can always be added back later – *www.webmd.com/diet/juicing-health-risks-and-benefits*). According to the Mayo Clinic, although there is 'no sound scientific evidence that extracted juices are healthier than the juice you get by eating the fruit or vegetable itself', extracting the juice in this way 'may be a fun way to add them to your diet or to try fruits and vegetables you normally wouldn't eat' (*www.mayoclinic.org/healthy-lifestyle/nutrition-and-healthy-eating/expert-answers/juicing/faq-20058020*). By comparison, a blender chops, purées and blends raw and cooked fruit and vegetables *while retaining the fibre*.

Make sure you always clean your appliance immediately after using it. This takes time, so plan for it. For me, cleaning my machine *immediately* and *preparing veggies and fruit for juicing ahead of time* were the two habits associated with juicing that were definitely worthwhile learning. Not cleaning your machine immediately will result in a build-up of bacteria, and as the bits and pieces harden it becomes so much more difficult to clean it. So clean the machine immediately!

Selecting ingredients

Due to the widespread use of pesticides it is always best to use the freshest organic fruit, vegetables and herbs that you have access to. Human exposure to pesticides can cause harm to various organs and systems of the body, especially among children, pregnant women and the elderly. Although various organisations monitor the use and types of pesticides in agriculture, health is still the individual's responsibility. If you are unable to buy organic produce you can still peel the selected fruit and veggies. Frozen produce is also a suitable substitute for fresh fruit and vegetables when making smoothies. Frozen berries are especially convenient to use on a hot day as they chill the smoothie too.

Plan your juices so that you can minimise produce wastage. A good rule of thumb is not to buy more than a week's supply of fruit and vegetables. Make sure to store them well to maintain freshness for longer.

Juicing could be a more expensive way of getting your daily fruit and vegetable intake, so try to use what is in season. Try to include one or two superfoods among your ingredients. Super-foods are those fruits, vegetables, nuts, legumes, herbs and spices that are nature's

most powerful sources of natural food for the human body. Taken in juice form these superfoods flood the body with life-giving vitamins, minerals, enzymes, antioxidants, phytonutrients and nutrients. I have found that the effects of a good juice can be felt almost immediately.

Juicing tips
- Make a list of the fruit and veg-

gies that you need before you go shopping so that you won't forget anything.

- When juicing in the morning, it may help to prepare your fruit and veggies the night before. Select the ingredients for your juice, wash and store the produce in your fridge and assemble the juicer in your kitchen so it's ready to go.
- Just before juicing, cut any items that might be too large to fit through the juicer. This speeds up the juicing time.
- Drink your juice as soon as possible because it starts to lose nutritional value almost immediately.
- Make more than one juice at a time and store in the fridge for up to 48 hours, but definitely not more than 72 hours. There are no preservatives in fresh juice so it has to be refrigerated or it can spoil quickly.
- Try, wherever possible, to fill your juice containers to the top. This prevents oxidation, which can deplete the nutrients.
- Using produce in season is more economical. Experiment with the combinations of veggies, fruit and herbs until you find what you like and what works for you. This should provide hours of joy.
- Depending on where in the world you live, juicing could be a more expensive way to health, but it is definitely worth incorporating into your lifestyle.

Superfoods

It is important for us to understand what is meant by the term 'superfoods'. If we turn to the dictionary for a definition of 'superfoods' we will find the following or similar: 'A nutrient-rich food considered to be especially beneficial for health and well-being.'[1]

That notwithstanding, there appears to be no official medical or scientific definition of a 'superfood' and little long-term credible research that conclusively supports the idea that 'eating a single fruit or vegetable containing a certain antioxidant will zap a diseased cell'.[2]

Free radicals are those chemicals that are known to cause cell damage. Unfortunately such chemicals are naturally produced in all living cells. Antioxidants are a different range of chemicals that are thought to protect against the harmful effects of the free radicals.

According to the UK's National Health Service online bulletin, NHS Choices, while 'diet plays an important role in our health . . . there is concern that too much focus on individual foods may encourage unhealthy eating'. It quotes dietitian Alison Hornby, spokesperson for the British Dietetic Association (BDA), as saying, 'No food, including those labelled "superfoods", can compensate for unhealthy eating.'[3]

The bulletin states that dietitians 'avoid the term "superfood" and prefer to talk of "super diets", where the emphasis is on a healthy, balanced diet, rich in fruit and vegetables and wholegrain foods'.[4]

As Hornby concludes: 'When it comes to keeping healthy, it's best not to concentrate on any one food in the hope it will work miracles. All unprocessed food from the major food groups could be considered "super". All these foods are useful as part of a balanced diet.'[5]

[1]http://www.oxforddictionaries.com/definition/english/superfood [2]http://www.nhs.uk/livewell/superfoods/pages/what-are-superfoods.aspx [3]Ibid. [4]Ibid. [5]Ibid.

Ingredients

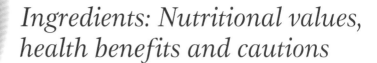

Ingredients: Nutritional values, health benefits and cautions

In this section I have tried to provide you with a fairly exhaustive list of the various ingredients I have used in order to create the juices and smoothies described in this book. They are arranged alphabetically and I have included some basic information under each heading that should be helpful to those of you who are interested in the health benefits associated with the various recipes.

This information could also be helpful to anyone wishing to create their own recipes, designed specifically to provide a given set of nutriments that may be required for themselves or someone else.

In order to provide you with a uniform set of nutritional values, health benefits and cautions (if and where necessary), I have chosen to source most of these from *http://www.medicalnewstoday.com*. Where I have drawn from other reputable sources the references are provided.

For those interested in delving deeper there is a wealth of more detailed information available through various respected and objective websites and printed publications.

In some instances I have included photographs of the ingredients, especially where they may be less familiar to some of our readers.

Almonds

Almonds are full of vitamins, minerals, protein and fibre, and are associated with a number of health benefits, particularly the improvement of cardiovascular health. Be aware that there is an allergy risk associated with the consumption of almonds.

Apples

Apples are one of the most widely cultivated and consumed fruits in the world. They are extremely rich in important antioxidants, flavonoids, and dietary fibre, and contain 'almost no fat, sodium or cholesterol'. It is also thought that the phytonutrients and antioxidants in apples may help to diminish the 'risk of developing cancer, hypertension, diabetes, and heart disease'.

There are no serious side effects linked to eating them except if one were to eat a large number of their seeds, which contain cyanide. Apples are acidic, however, and their juice can be 'four times more damaging to teeth than carbonated drinks'. This is a caution that should be heeded when one does a lot of juicing using acidic fruits.

Apricots

Apricots are considered to be a great food that provides you with the protective effects of antioxidants while adding very few calories to your daily total. They are a good source of dietary fibre as well, of which about half consists of soluble fibre – one type that can help control blood cholesterol levels (*www.whfoods.org*).

Avocado

According to the USDA National Nutrient Database, 'One serving (one-fifth of an avocado, approximately 40 grams) contains 64 calories, 6 grams of fat, 4 grams of carbohydrate, 0 grams of sugar, 3 grams of fibre and 1 gram of protein.' Avocados are also a good source of vitamins C, E, K, and B6, as well as riboflavin, niacin, folate, pantothenic acid, magnesium, potassium, and lutein, beta-carotene and omega-3s.

Bananas

It is a little-known fact that bananas are naturally free of fat and cholesterol, and contain only minimal amounts of sodium, making them a very healthy food option. They also provide a variety of vitamins and minerals.

Research into their benefit is ongoing but a study conducted by 'the Imperial College of London found that children who ate just one banana per day had a 34% less chance of developing asthma'. Other studies suggest that bananas 'also contain tryptophan, an amino acid that . . . plays a role in preserving memory and boosting your mood'.

Beetroot

Beetroot is gaining popularity as a new 'superfood' due to recent studies claiming that it can improve athletic performance, lower blood pressure and increase blood flow. It is of the same family as sugar beets (*Beta vulgaris*), but is both genetically and nutritionally different. Sugar cannot be obtained from beetroot, which is most commonly found in red and gold varieties. Beetroot is high in dietary nitrate, which is believed to be one of the reasons why it appears to improve athletic performance. (See *www.ncbi.nlm.nih.gov/pubmed/22709704.*)

Take note of the fact that 'a high-nitrate diet may interact with certain medications such as organic nitrate (nitroglycerin) or nitrite drugs used for angina, sildenafil citrate, tadalafil, and vardenafil'. Also be aware that the consumption of beetroot and beetroot juice often leads to red-coloured urine and stools.

Three a day dissolves the weight away!

According to Medical News Today* a recent study, which appeared in the journal *Obesity*, found that 'drinking 500ml of water half an hour before eating breakfast, lunch and dinner led to greater weight loss among obese adults compared with those who did not drink water before mealtimes'.

The research, conducted by the University of Birmingham (UK), found that 'preloading' with 500ml of tap water 30 minutes before meals led to a 1.3kg-greater average weight loss per participant over 12 weeks.

Although not exactly sure of why this happens, Dr Helen Parretti suggests that the water may increase our metabolism temporarily or make us feel fuller so that we eat less. She added this caution, however: 'There are some groups of patients, such as those with heart or kidney failure, for whom consuming a pint of water before mealtimes may not be appropriate.'

*http://www.medicalnewstoday.com/articles/298627.php

Blackberries

Sweet, succulent blackberries (*Rubus fruticosus*) are regarded as summer delicacies in the northern temperate regions. Like raspberries, they grow on shrubs known as 'brambles'. Blackberries are an 'aggregate fruit' comprising small drupelets arranged in a circular fashion. Each drupelet consists of juicy pulp surrounding a single tiny seed, with 80-100 drupelets forming each berry.

Blackberries are full of plant nutrients such as vitamins, minerals, antioxidants, and dietary fibres that are essential for good health. They are also very low in calories (*www.nutrition-and-you.com*).

Broccoli

Broccoli is one of the best veggies you can put on your plate. It belongs to the cruciferous vegetable family, which includes kale, cauliflower, Brussels sprouts, bok choy, cabbage, collard greens, rutabaga and turnips. These powerhouse vegetables supply loads of nutrients for few calories. For example, one cup of broccoli will provide over 100% of your daily need for vitamin C and vitamin K, and is also a good source of vitamin A, folate and potassium.

'Eating a high amount of cruciferous vegetables has been associated with a lower risk of cancer: namely, lung and colon cancer'. Although more clinical trials are needed, some 'studies have suggested that sulforaphane, the sulfur-containing compound that gives cruciferous vegetables their bitter bite, is also what gives them their cancer-fighting power'.

Those taking blood-thinners such as warfarin should be aware that a sudden and sustained increase in consumption of foods containing vitamin K might affect them negatively.

Butternut

The USDA National Nutrient Database lists one cup of cooked butternut (approximately 205 grams) as containing 82 calories, 0 grams of fat and 22 grams of carbohydrate (including 4 grams of sugar and 6.6 grams of dietary fibre), as well as 1.8 grams of protein. That quantity of butternut will supply 437% of your vitamin A needs for the day, as well as '52% of vitamin C and 10% or more of vitamin E, thiamin, niacin, vitamin B6, folate, pantothenic acid, magnesium and manganese'. Gram for gram it provides more potassium than bananas do!

Cabbage

Cruciferous vegetables like cabbage, kale and broccoli are full of beneficial nutrients.

Eating a half-cup of cooked cabbage will provide 47% of your recommended daily allowance (RDA) of vitamin C. It will also provide 102% of vitamin K, 8% of manganese, 6% of folate and lesser amounts of vitamin B6, calcium, potassium and thiamin. Cabbage also contains a number of important antioxidants.

Many studies have suggested that increasing our intake of plant foods like cabbage decreases our risk of obesity, diabetes, heart disease and cancer.

Those taking blood-thinners such as warfarin should be aware that a sudden increase or decrease in consumption of foods containing vitamin K might affect them negatively.

Carrots

Purple, red, yellow and white carrots were cultivated long before the popular orange carrot, which was developed by the Dutch in the sixteenth and seventeenth centuries. Carrots are often thought of as the ultimate health food. An overwhelming body of evidence exists suggesting that an increased intake of antioxidant-rich fruits and vegetables helps to reduce cancer and cardiovascular disease risks, carrots included. Half a cup will supply 210% of the average adult's RDA of vitamin A, 6% of vitamin C, 2% of calcium and 2% of iron. Carrots also contain fibre, vitamin K, potassium, folate, manganese, phosphorus, magnesium, vitamin E and zinc.

'Carrots are best stored in the refrigerator in a sealed plastic bag. If the greens are still attached to the top of the carrot, remove them before storing to prevent the greens from drawing out moisture and nutrients from the roots. Carrots should be peeled and washed before consuming.'

Overconsumption of carotene may cause a slight orange tinge in skin colour but is not harmful to health.

Cashews

Cashews are a good source of monounsaturated fats and proteins. They are also packed with vitamins and minerals, which is also another reason for consuming them. Research has revealed that 75% of the fat present in cashews is composed of unsaturated fatty acids, and 75% of this unsaturated fat is monounsaturated oleic acid. 'Studies reveal that oleic acid promotes heart health, thereby keeping cardiovascular diseases at bay.' It is important to bear in mind, however, that while fat from these nuts 'is primarily the healthier type of fat, even that may lead to weight gain if eaten in excess'.

Cashews have zero cholesterol content and, based on *in vitro* studies, they are believed to help destroy the bacteria responsible for tooth decay and gum diseases.

Consult your nutritionist or physician if you are concerned about any possible side effects because cashew allergies 'carry a higher risk of anaphylaxis than other nut allergies'. If your 'face and throat swell and you experience breathing problems after eating cashews, you need immediate emergency medical care' (*www.seedguides.info/cashew-nuts*).

Cauliflower
Cauliflower is part of the brassica family and contains antioxidants and phytonutrients that are thought to protect against cancer, although more research is required. It is also high in fibre, with the associated benefit that it promotes regularity. Eating one cup of raw cauliflower will provide 77% of your vitamin C needs, 20% of vitamin K, and 10% or more of vitamin B6 and folate needs for the day, as well as smaller amounts of thiamin, riboflavin, niacin, pantothenic acid, calcium, iron, magnesium, phosphorus, potassium and manganese.

Those taking blood-thinners such as warfarin should be aware that a sudden increase or decrease in consumption of foods containing vitamin K might affect them negatively.

Cayenne pepper
Cayenne pepper is a hot chilli pepper, often used in spicy dishes. It has been associated with a wide range of health benefits. What gives the chilli its spiciness is the active ingredient capsaicin, which is used to treat aches and pains of the muscles and joints. It also contains vitamin C, vitamin B6, vitamin E, potassium, manganese, and flavonoids.

Using cayenne at the same time as ACE inhibitors (such as Captopril and Elaroptril) can increase the risk of cough. It has been known to promote the secretion of stomach acid.

Celery
Celery is a vegetable of the *Apiaceae* family that makes a good low-calorie snack. It is thought to be beneficial for the digestive tract and cardiovascular system, as well as being

a very rich source of antioxidants. Celery contains the following phytonutrients: phenolic acids, flavonols, dihydrostilbenoids, flavones, furanocoumarins, and phytosterols. It is very rich in vitamin K and also contains folate, vitamin A, potassium, and vitamin C.

Cherries

The website *www.nutrition-and-you.com* makes the following assessment of the benefits of this fruit: 'Cherries are one of the very low-calorie fruits. Nonetheless, they are a rich source of phytonutrients, vitamins, and minerals. Both sweet as well as tart cherries are packed with numerous health-benefiting compounds that are essential for wellness.'

It goes on to say that the fruit contains the antioxidant melatonin, which 'can cross the blood-brain barrier easily and has soothing effects on the brain neurons, calming down nervous system irritability'.

Some studies have shown them to be high in cyanidin, an antioxidant that may have a role in cancer prevention. Other studies have shown them to have an anti-inflammatory effect that may soothe gout, arthritis and muscle pain in general.

Chia seeds

'Despite their small size, chia seeds are packed full of important nutrients. They are an excellent source of omega-3 fatty acids, which help to raise HDL cholesterol (the good cholesterol that helps protect against heart attack and stroke).' One ounce of chia seeds per day will provide '18% of daily calcium needs, 27% of phosphorus, 30% of manganese and smaller amounts of potassium, zinc and copper'.

There are some studies which suggest that the regular use of chia seeds in cases of type 2 diabetes may be beneficial in reducing blood pressure. (See *http://m.care. diabetesjournals.org/content/ 30/11/2804.long.*)

Cinnamon

Cinnamon is a spice that comes from the branches of wild trees that belong to the genus *Cinnamomum* and there are two main types, with Chinese cinnamon being less expensive than the more sought-after Ceylon cinnamon.

Some studies have shown promising results in type 2 diabetics who take 1-6g of cinnamon daily: namely, reduction in total cholesterol, LDL or 'bad' cholesterol and triglyceride levels.

Be aware that people who are sensitive to cinnamon may be at 'an increased risk of liver damage after consuming cinnamon-flavoured foods, drinks and food supplements'. This is probably due to coumarin, which has been linked to liver damage. Ceylon cinnamon contains less coumarin than Chinese cinnamon.

Clementine

According to *www.dovemed.com*, the clementine is a hybrid between a mandarin and a sweet orange. The peel is generally a dark orange colour and has a smooth, glossy appearance. This fruit is an excellent source of vitamin C; the B-vitamin complex; and potassium – but is low in sodium (a distinct advantage).

Cocoa

Many people crave chocolate and avoid it because they are under the impression that it is fattening, calorie-dense and unhealthy, which a lot of chocolate products are. This is due to the addition of substances such as sugar and not to the cocoa itself. In fact, cocoa powder, which comes from the cocoa bean, is highly nutritious, and it can provide numerous health benefits.

According to *www.livestrong.com*, however, most commercial cocoa powders have the antioxidant-containing flavonoids removed because they taste bitter; therefore, 'in order to obtain the health-boosting benefits, consider buying raw cocoa powder', which has been minimally processed.

Be aware, though, that cocoa contains caffeine,

which means that it may have negative side effects on caffeine-sensitive people.

Coconut
Coconuts are highly nutritious and rich in fibre, vitamins C, E, B1, B3, B5 and B6 and a variety of important minerals. Coconut milk is lactose free and can be used as a milk substitute by those with lactose intolerance. It is also a popular choice with vegans and the lower-fat variety makes a great base for smoothies.

Be aware, however, that because of 'coconut milk's high content of saturated fatty acids, it is still seen as a food that should be consumed in moderation' (*www.bbcgoodfood.com*).

Coriander/cilantro
Coriander (*Coriandrum sativum*) is a herb most of us are familiar with. In the United States, the leaves of the plant are referred to as cilantro (the Spanish translation) and the seeds are referred to as coriander. The leaves are also referred to as Chinese parsley. If you have a choice, buy whole seeds instead of coriander powder, because the latter often contains adulterated ingredients.

Cranberries
As far as healthy foods go, cranberries are at the top of the list due to their high nutrient and antioxidant content and are often referred to as a 'superfood', especially when you

consider that half a cup contains only 25 calories!

Cranberries are also high in vitamin C and fibre, but what really sets them apart from other fruits is their wide array of phytonutrients – which have been found to offer anti-inflammatory and antioxidant benefits.

Be aware that those with 'a history of kidney stones should talk to their healthcare provider before including any forms of cranberries in their diet'.

Cucumber

Cucumbers belong to the *Cucurbitaceae* botanical family, as do honeydew melons, cantaloupes and watermelons. They typically consist of 95% water and are low in calories, fat, cholesterol and sodium. Their regular use will help prevent dehydration and maintain healthy bowel function. One cup of cucumber provides the following RDA proportions: 11% of vitamin K (vital for calcium absorption), 4% of vitamin C, magnesium, potassium and manganese and 2% of vitamin A, thiamin, riboflavin, B6, folate, pantothenic acid, calcium, iron, phosphorus, zinc and copper.

Cucumbers also contain lignans that, as research has indicated, may diminish the risk of cardiovascular disease and certain forms of cancer.

Cucumbers are high on the pesticide residue list of the Environmental Working Group (EWG). Suggestion: buy organic if you can or wash produce carefully (*http://www.ewg.org/foodnews/dirty_dozen_list.php*).

Dates

This delicious fruit is rich in dietary fibre, which prevents LDL cholesterol absorption in the gut. The fibre also works as a bulk laxative, helping to protect the colon mucous membrane from cancer-causing chemicals binding to it. Dates are also rich in minerals like iron, calcium, manganese, copper, and magnesium, all of which are essential to the optimum functioning of the human body.

Dates replenish energy and revitalise the body instantly due to their fructose content, which is why they have been used by Muslims since ancient times as the food with which to break the fast during the month of Ramadan (*www.nutrition-and-you.com*).

Garlic

Although garlic (*Allium sativum*), a close relative of the onion, rakkyo, chive, leek, and shallot, is a herb commonly used in cooking, it is also used widely today for its therapeutic properties. There is a growing body of research that suggests that garlic has potential health benefits in a number of areas, but it appears best known for its antibiotic properties – particularly as a prophylactic that decreases the frequency of common colds among adults.

Historians claim that garlic was also used in ancient India as an aphrodisiac. Apparently the wealthy avoided it for its strong odour, while monks, 'widows, adolescents and those who had taken up a vow or were fasting could not eat garlic because of its stimulant quality'.

Ginger

Ginger has long been used to relieve digestive problems and it is part of the *Zingiberaceae* family, as are cardamom and turmeric. Studies have shown that the phenolic compounds in ginger help relieve gastrointestinal irritation, stimulate saliva and bile production and 'suppress gastric contractions and movement of food and fluids through the GI tract'. It also contains beneficial anti-inflammatory and antioxidant compounds such as gingerols, beta-carotene, capsaicin, caffeic acid, curcumin and salicylate.

There is also promising evidence that ginger may help improve blood glucose control among type 2 diabetics.

Natural ginger causes few, if any, side effects, but may worsen the symptoms of acid reflux for some.

Grapefruit

Grapefruits are low in calories but full of nutrients. Eating half of a grapefruit per day will meet 64% of your vitamin C needs, 28% of vitamin A, 2% of calcium and 2% of magnesium.

Pink grapefruit is high in common vitamins and minerals, and rich in antioxidants, specifically lycopene and beta-carotene, along with the phytonutrients limonoids and naringenin. 'Studies have shown that fresh pink or red grapefruit contains higher quantities of bioactive compounds and has significantly higher antioxidant potential than white or yellow grapefruit.'

Be aware that grapefruit intake should be avoided when taking certain medications because it can cause them to pass into your bloodstream faster than they should. The higher concentration of these medications can be dangerous. 'Statin drugs, calcium channel blockers and psychiatric drugs are some of the most-common medications that interact with grapefruit.'

Greek yoghurt
Yoghurt generally comes from milk. This means that it contains animal protein and several other nutrients found in dairy foods, like calcium, vitamin B2, vitamin B12, potassium, and magnesium. Yoghurt also contains probiotics, 'friendly bacteria' that are naturally present in the digestive system. Live strains of these 'good bacteria' are also found in many yoghurt products, and there is gathering evidence that 'some strains of probiotics can help boost the immune system and promote a healthy digestive tract' (*www.webmd.com*).

Studies have shown that the consumption of the 'live probiotics' present in some yoghurts can protect against antibiotic-associated diarrhoea and lessen the symptoms of IBS (irritable bowel syndrome).

If you support the growing trend to reduce or eliminate the use of dairy products – something that is being advised by many dieticians – there is an expanding range of dairy-free alternatives for you to choose from. In fact there are many parts of the world where non-dairy yoghurt is already freely available from local supermarkets at

Yoghurt varieties

Although yoghurt is produced in a wide variety of flavours, forms and textures, there are three basic types: regular (at least 3.25% milk fat), low-fat (low-fat milk or semi-skimmed milk, between 2 and 0.5 percent milk fat) and non-fat (less than 0.5% percent milk fat).

Yoghurt labelled as containing 'active yoghurt cultures' is thought to provide yoghurt with its many desirable healthful properties and is preferred over that which has had the beneficial live and active yoghurt cultures killed off by heating.

Source: *http://aboutyogurt.com/index.asp?bid=27* (the official site of the US National Yogurt Association)

competitive prices. There are also a number of websites that offer excellent help to those who want to make their own non-dairy yoghurt, for example *http://www.culturesfor health.com.*

Green grapes

Grapes are actually considered to be berries and upwards of 72 million tons of them are grown worldwide each year. According to recent research, 'The high polyphenol content in grapes [found mainly in the skin] may also reduce the risk of cardiovascular disease (CVD) by preventing platelet build-up and reducing blood pressure via anti-inflammatory mechanisms.'

Owing to their high potassium content, grapes are recommended for those with high blood pressure to help counter the effects of sodium in the body. Grapes are also high in water content and good for hydration.

Hazelnuts

These nuts are very high in energy (100g yield 628 calories) and packed with beneficial nutrients essential for optimum health. They are rich in monounsaturated fatty acids like oleic acid as well as the essential fatty acid, linoleic acid, which helps lower LDL (bad) cholesterol and raise HDL (good) cholesterol levels (*www.nutrition-and-you.com*).

Honey

Honey contains high levels of monosaccharides, fructose and glucose, which means that it comprises about 70 to 80 percent sugar. This gives it the sweet taste, while minerals and water make up the rest of its composition. It is well known that honey possesses antiseptic and antibacterial properties, and modern scientists are gradually making further discoveries that confirm the wisdom of King Solomon's statement, 'My son, eat thou honey, because it is good' (Proverbs 24:13, KJV).

Although there is some evidence that honey may offer some benefits over refined sugar, if you are trying to lose weight or control your diabetes, honey may exacerbate these problems.

Kale

Kale is so packed with nutrition that it ranks high on the list of the world's healthiest foods. So much so that it even beats spinach as a source of nutrients. For this reason it has many possible health benefits that include the improvement of blood-glucose control in diabetics, lowering the risk of cancer, lowering blood pressure and improving bone health.

One cup of raw kale provides over 100% of our recommended daily allowance of vitamin C, over 600% of our vitamin K RDA, and over 200% of our beta-carotene needs. Unlike spinach, kale's oxalate content is very low, which means that the calcium and iron in kale are absorbed more readily by our digestive systems.

Kiwi fruit

The kiwi fruit, initially known as the Chinese gooseberry, was brought to New Zealand from northern China at the turn of the twentieth century. These fruits are high in nutrients and low in calories.

According to a study on the effects of kiwi fruit consumption it was found that it may improve sleep onset, duration, and efficiency in adults. Regular consumption of kiwi fruit was shown to promote bulkier, softer and more frequent stools. The fruit is higher in vitamin C per ounce than most fruits – including oranges and lemons. It is known to improve heart health and may also lower blood pressure in conjunction with a healthy balanced diet.

Lemons

One fluid ounce of lemon juice provides 7 calories, 0.1 grams of protein, 0.1 grams of fat, 2.1 grams of carbohydrate (including 0.1 grams of fibre and 0.1 grams of sugar) and 23% of our daily vitamin C needs. It also contains small amounts of thiamin, riboflavin, vitamin B6, pantothenic acid, calcium, iron, magnesium, phosphorus, potassium, copper and manganese.

Lemons are full of the powerful antioxidant, vitamin C, and this can help fight the formation of free radicals that are known to cause cancer. Vitamin C is also known to play a special role in the formation of collagen, the support system of your skin, and to assist in the body's absorption of iron, not to mention the way it strengthens the immune system in its battle with colds and flu.

Citric acid may also help reduce the risk of developing kidney stones.

Lemongrass

Lemongrass (also known as citronella) has a lemony taste and is a popular flavour in Asian cuisine. It is also used to

scent perfumes and insect repellants. It's less well known for its antifungal and antibacterial properties – the ability to inhibit bacteria and yeast growth. For this reason it is considered useful during certain gastrointestinal infections (*www.healthers.org/lemongrass*).

Lettuce

It is interesting to note that lettuce has a low calorie content and almost zero fat: 'only 12 calories for one shredded cup'. This makes it great for 'anyone watching their blood sugars for medical reasons, or for weight management' (*www.foodshealthfacts.com*).

Mangoes

The mango is a member of the drupe family, a plant in which an outer fleshy part surrounds a shell (what we sometimes call a pit) with a seed inside: other examples of which are olives, dates and coconuts. Mangoes are found in a wide range of colours, shapes, flavours and sizes – and are regarded by some as the 'most widely consumed fruit in the world'.

Be aware that those with a 'latex allergy' may also have a cross-reaction to mangoes.

Milk

Milk contains almost all the nutrients our bodies require. It is especially high in protein which contains the majority of the essential amino acids. Studies have also shown that the regular intake of milk can lower blood pressure. A cup of whole

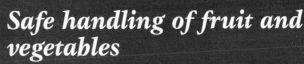

Safe handling of fruit and vegetables

- Always wash your hands thoroughly before and after handling raw food, including vegetables.
- Keep raw food, including vegetables, separate from ready-to-eat foods.
- Use different chopping boards, knives and utensils for raw and ready-to-eat foods, or wash these items thoroughly in between uses.
- Check the label – unless packaging around vegetables says 'ready to eat', you must wash, peel or cook them before eating.

Source: *http://www.nhs.uk/Livewell/homehygiene/Pages/How-to-wash-fruit-and-vegetables.aspx*

milk (one serving) with 3.25% fat contains 146 calories, 8 grams of fat, 13 grams of carbohydrate and 8 grams of protein, while a serving of non-fat or skimmed milk has about 86 calories, 0 grams of fat, 12 grams of carbohydrate and 8 grams of protein. Dairy products like milk are the best dietary sources of calcium, the primary role of which is the development and maintenance of healthy bones and teeth. Calcium is also important for blood clotting and wound healing, maintaining normal blood pressure, and muscle contractions, including heartbeats.

Be aware that some people are lactose intolerant, while others may suffer from a milk allergy with symptoms such as 'asthma, eczema (an itchy rash), rhinitis (inflamed nose), and gastrointestinal distress, as well as bleeding, pneumonia, and even anaphylaxis (shock)'.

There is a body of widespread and scientifically supported opinion that a carefully balanced vegan diet may actually be preferable to one that is heavily dependent on the various forms of animal protein, including the use of dairy products. This is borne out by the fact that the 'societies which use the most dairy products also have the highest rates of chronic degenerative disease'.* The reader is therefore encouraged to experiment with suitable non-dairy alternatives, especially those with a low fat and sugar content.

Understanding Nutrition, by Dr Clemency Mitchell, page 90 (The Stanborough Press Ltd)

Mint

Mint is actually a genus or group of up to 30 types of plants, including peppermint and spearmint. Mint oil is used in toothpaste, gum, sweets and various beauty products, and the leaves can be used for teas and food, in either fresh or dried form.

Mint plants contain an antioxidant known as rosmarinic acid, which appears to be effective in relieving seasonal allergy symptoms. It also contains menthol, a natural decongestant that breaks up phlegm and mucus.

Do not use mint to soothe gastroesophageal reflux diease. Peppermint oil, if taken in large doses, can be toxic. Ask your doctor if mint could interfere with any of your medications.

Oats

Oats are rich in a specific type of fibre called beta-glucan, which is known to help lower the levels of bad cholesterol.

They also contain a host of essential minerals and vitamins, while providing a good source of calories too – one cup of dry oats (81g) contains approximately 307 calories.

The potential health benefits of oats include: reducing the risk of coronary artery disease, lowering levels of cholesterol, and reducing one's risk of colorectal cancer. They may also help to lower blood pressure.

Oranges

An orange a day is a great idea because they are low in calories but full of nutrients. Orange trees are the most cultivated fruit trees in the world, and oranges are a popular fruit because of their natural sweetness, wide variety of types and diversity of uses – from juices and marmalades to candied orange slices.

On average each orange contains over 170 different phytochemicals and more than 60 flavonoids, many of which have been shown to have anti-inflammatory properties and strong antioxidant effects. One orange provides 130 percent of your vitamin C needs for the day, 2 percent of vitamin A needs, 6 percent of calcium and 0 percent of iron. Because of this high vitamin C content (more than the daily requirement) oranges are also associated with the boosting of our immune systems.

Papaya

Papayas, also known as papaws or pawpaws, are widely available these days and are valued for their sweet taste, vibrant colour and wide variety of health benefits. Among the many excellent things they contain is choline, a very important and versatile nutrient that aids our bodies in sleep, muscle movement, learning and memory. 'Choline also helps to maintain the structure of cellular membranes, aids in the transmission of nerve impulses, assists in the absorption of fat and reduces chronic inflammation.'

Parsley

Parsley is often an afterthought – used to enhance the flavour or presentation of a dish – but it is also a way to simultaneously provide additional nutrients and health benefits. For example, myricetin is a flavonol found in

parsley that has been shown to protect against cancer and diabetes.

Peaches

One fresh medium peach (147 grams) has 50 calories, 0.5 grams of fat, 0 grams of cholesterol and sodium, 15 grams of carbohydrate, 13 grams of sugar, 2 grams of fibre and 1 gram of protein. It provides 6% of your daily vitamin A needs and 15% of daily vitamin C needs.

One medium peach also contains 2% or more of the daily value of vitamins E and K, niacin, folate, iron, choline, potassium, magnesium, phosphorus, manganese, zinc and copper we require.

Peanut butter

According to a credible source, 'Peanut butter is high in fat and calories (with around 190 calories and 16 grams of fat per 2 tablespoons)' but it is very nutritious. It goes on to state: 'Nuts and nut butters are a great source of protein, fibre, vitamins, minerals, and phytochemicals.'

Although high in fat, and therefore calories, it is rich in monounsaturates, which have a positive effect on cholesterol levels – but needs to be used judiciously if you are watching your weight.

As far as smoothies are concerned it suggests that peanut

Phytonutrients

The plants we use for food contain thousands of 'natural chemicals' called phytonutrients or phytochemicals. The term 'phyto' is the Greek word for plant and it indicates both the source of these nutrients and chemicals and the fact that they help 'protect plants from germs, fungi, bugs, and other threats'.

Fruits and vegetables contain phytonutrients, as do wholegrains, nuts, beans and tea. These aren't essential for keeping humans alive, unlike the vitamins and minerals that such foods contain. When we eat or drink these phytonutrients, however, 'they may help prevent disease' and keep our bodies working properly.

Source: http://www.webmd.com/diet/guide/phytonutrients-faq

butter be added to them, especially if they are 'chocolate-or banana-flavoured'. It goes without saying that the more natural the brand is, the better (*http://www.webmd.com/food-recipes/nutty-about-peanut-butter*).

Pears/green pears
Pears are rich in antioxidants, flavonoids and dietary fibre, and package all of those nutrients in a fat-free, cholesterol-free, high-energy package. It is also suggested that pears may help with weight loss and reduce the risk of

developing cancer, hypertension, diabetes, and heart disease, in accordance with an overall healthy diet.

One medium pear will provide 12% of your daily vitamin C needs, as well as 10% of vitamin K, 6% of potassium and smaller amounts of calcium, iron, magnesium, riboflavin, vitamin B6 and folate.

Persimmon

Persimmon fruit is moderately high in calories (70 calories/100g) but very low in fats. Its smooth textured flesh is a very good source of dietary fibre and it contains a wide range of essential nutrients, minerals, flavonoids, vitamins, and so on.

Pineapples

One cup of fresh pineapple chunks will provide 131% of your vitamin C needs for the day, 2% of vitamin A needs, 2% of calcium and 2% of iron. Fresh pineapple is the only known source of an enzyme called bromelain, and some studies have indicated that this enzyme can reduce the swelling, bruising, healing time and pain associated with injury and surgery.

Pumpkin

Pumpkin is a very nutrient-dense food – it is full of vitamins and minerals but low on calories. In fact, *'One cup of cooked, canned pumpkin would provide well over 100% of your daily needs for vitamin A, 20% of the daily value for vitamin C, 10% or more for vitamin E, riboflavin, potassium, copper and manganese, and at least 5% for thiamin, B6, folate, pantothenic acid, niacin, iron, magnesium, and phosphorus.'*

Pumpkin is an excellent source of beta-carotene, a powerful antioxidant that is converted to vitamin A in the body. Consuming beta-carotene rich foods may reduce the risk of developing certain types of cancer and offer protection against asthma and heart disease.

Radishes

Radishes are an edible root vegetable that is part of the *Brassicaceae* family, and they are widely used in dishes from around the world. They may vary in flavour, colour, size and shape. They have a high water content of around 90%; and a wide range of essential vitamins and minerals. Radishes are also known to have both antifungal and antibacterial properties.

Raisins

Raisins have numerous health benefits but one that is really worth mentioning is their high iron content, which assists in counteracting anaemia. They also contain vitamins of the B complex that are essential for the formation of new blood. Their high copper content also helps in the formation of red blood cells.

Studies have shown that eating raisins as part of a balanced diet may help lower blood pressure, help blood sugar control and reduce cholesterol levels.

Red bell peppers

Bell peppers are an excellent source of carotenoids –

containing over thirty different members of the carotenoid nutrient family. For example, just one cup of sweet green bell pepper slices will provide us with 314 micrograms (combined) of the carotenoids lutein and zeaxanthin. These specific carotenoids are found in high concentrations in the macula of the eye (the centremost part of the retina), and they are required in order to protect the macula from oxygen-related damage (*www.whfoods.com*).

Rocket (arugula)

Rocket, also known as arugula and rucola, is a less-recognised member of the cruciferous family (broccoli, kale and Brussels sprouts) that is very high in nitrates but low in calories. It is among the top foods on the Aggregate Nutrient Density Index (ANDI), which means that it is high in vitamins, minerals and phytonutrients in relation to its caloric content.

'Consuming 2 cups of arugula will provide 20% of vitamin A, over 50% of vitamin K and 8% of your vitamin C, folate and calcium needs for the day.'

Spinach

Dark leafy greens like spinach are important for skin, hair and bone health. They provide iron, vitamins and minerals. One cup of raw spinach contains 27 calories, 0.86 grams of protein, 30 milligrams of calcium, 0.81 grams of iron, 24 milligrams of magnesium, 167 milligrams of potassium, 2,813 IUs of vitamin A and 58 micrograms of folate. Spinach is also one of the best sources of dietary potassium, weighing in at 839mg per cup (cooked). To compare, one cup of banana has about 539mg of potassium.

These are some of the possible health benefits associated with spinach: healthier skin and hair; improved blood-glucose control in diabetics; lowering of the risk of cancer; reduced blood pressure; and improved bone and eye health.

Strawberries

Fresh summer strawberries are certainly a popular, refreshing and healthy treat. Worldwide there are over 600 varieties of strawberries to choose from and they are rich in vitamin C, potassium, folic acid and fibre. One cup of fresh strawberries contains 160% of your daily needs for vitamin C, for only 50 calories!

Strawberries are a low-glycaemic-index food that is high

in fibre, which helps to regulate blood sugar by avoiding extreme highs and lows. Be aware that they are high on the EWG pesticide list, which means that you should make sure that they are well washed, regardless of whether they are organically farmed or not.

Sweet melon (cantaloupe)
'Cantaloupes and other summer melons serve as the quintessential take-along snack for summer picnics and barbeques. Their high water content helps ward off dehydration and combat the heat while their refreshing taste provides a guilt-free, low-maintenance dessert for kids and adults alike.' The mildly sweet and juicy flavour of cantaloupe makes it a perfect fruit for juices and smoothies.

'The antioxidant zeaxanthin, found in cantaloupe, filters out harmful blue light rays and is thought to play a protective role in eye health and possibly ward off damage from macular degeneration.'

Sweet potatoes
Sweet potatoes are very nutritious. One medium potato will provide over 400% of your daily vitamin A requirement, along with loads of fibre and potassium. They contain more grams of natural sugars than regular potatoes, but more overall nutrients with fewer calories.

Sweet potatoes and yams are often confused with each other but they are not related. Yams are almost exclusively grown in Africa and are more dry and starchy than sweet

potatoes. There are two varieties of sweet potatoes, firm and soft.

The colour of sweet potato skin can vary from white to yellow, purple or brown, but no matter what colour it is, try not to peel it off, because it contains significant amounts of fibre, potassium and quercetin.

Swiss chard

Swiss chard is highly nutritious, and provides over 700% of our daily vitamin K requirement along with over 200% of vitamin A needs, all in a single cup. That single serving (175 grams) also supplies the following portions of our RDA: 53% of vitamin C, 38% of magnesium, 29% of manganese, 27% of potassium, 22% of iron and 17% of vitamin E. It also holds smaller amounts of thiamin, riboflavin, niacin, pantothenic acid, vitamin B6, calcium, phosphorus, zinc

and selenium. Swiss chard is also known as silverbeet, spinach beet, perpetual spinach, crab beet and mangold.

'According to a 2013 study published in the British Journal of Clinical Pharmacology, foods high in dietary nitrates like Swiss chard have been shown to have multiple vascular benefits, including reducing blood pressure. . . .' The same is true of its ability to improve muscle oxygenation during exercise.

Those taking blood-thinners such as warfarin should be aware that a sudden increase or decrease in consumption of foods containing vitamin K might affect them negatively.

Tofu

Tofu is made from soybean curds, is low in calories, contains no cholesterol and is an excellent source of protein, iron, and calcium. It has become an important source of protein for vegans, vegetarians and those looking for a more plant-based diet. 'Soy is the prime component of tofu and is a complete source of dietary protein providing all of the essential amino acids needed in the diet.'

Tofu is rich in iron and calcium but also

contains small amounts of vitamin K, thiamin, riboflavin, niacin, vitamin B6, folate, choline, phosphorus, manganese and selenium.

Watermelon

Watermelon is made up of more than just water and sugar. It provides a high concentration of vitamins, minerals and antioxidants for a low amount of calories. 'One cup of diced watermelon (152 grams) contains 43 calories, 0 grams of fat, 2 milligrams of sodium, 11 grams of carbohydrate (including 9 grams of sugar) and 1 gram of fibre,' plus the added bonus of '17% of vitamin A, 21% of vitamin C, 2% of iron and 1% of [our] calcium needs for the day.'

Comprising 92% water and full of important electrolytes, watermelon is a great snack for those hot summer months.

Benefits and cautions at a glance

For many of our readers the primary motivation for obtaining this book will be their desire to try out some innovative, tasty and invigorating food combinations. There are others, however, who may be looking for recipes with ingredients that will boost their immune systems, help improve their digestion, put the shine back in their lacklustre hair or entice their children to eat more wholesome fresh fruit and vegetables.

Some among this second group may even be searching for drinks they can serve to their ailing or recuperating loved ones. For this reason they will be looking for fruit, vegetable, herb, spice and nut combinations that are packed with the vitamins, minerals and phytonutrients to nourish them back to health.

The handy set of icons set out below will help the reader easily identify both the health benefits and the occasional cautions associated with each of the 102 recipes in this book. The icons indicate that there are ingredients in that recipe containing the micronutrients and macronutrients associated with either a benefit or a caution.*

Benefits:

 Cardiovascular/blood quality

 Digestion/elimination

 Eyesight

 Hair/skin

 Joint mobility/anti-inflammatory

 Mind/nervous system

 Physical fitness/energy

Cautions:

 Interaction with medication

*Micronutrients consist of vitamins and minerals that are needed in small quantities to ensure normal metabolism, growth and general physical well-being. By contrast, macronutrients are the proteins, carbohydrates and fats that our bodies require.

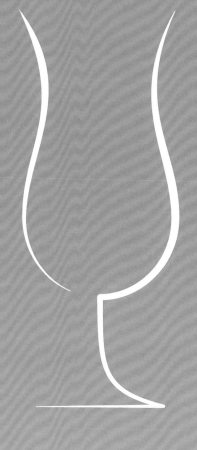

Juices

Green juices

'Drinking just one freshly pressed juice each day is a reliable way of infusing your body with a wide variety of vitamins, minerals, and phytonutrients that can protect your cells against premature ageing and disease.' – Dr Ben Kim

The benefits of juicing are numerous; there is no question about it. But why the fuss about green juices? Is this just a fad, a status symbol, or is a green juice perhaps superior to other juices? Mariam Turay describes its benefits well when she says that green juices are 'alkalising, cleansing, healing, hydrating and restorative'.[1]

They are packed with nutrients, vitamins, minerals and phytonutrients, which are transported directly to the cells, instantly providing the body with health and energy.

Green juice made only with green vegetables can be an acquired taste. This is easily remedied by adding carrot, apple, pear or various herbs for flavour. Feel free to experiment with combinations until you discover what your body likes.

That's what we're aiming at.

[1]*www.greenjuiceaday.com*

The cleansing Cs

Cucumber and celery are not the best taste combination that you will find, but adding ginger and lemon gives this juice a refreshing zestiness. This is a very basic green juice.

Benefits: Cucumber and celery help to flush out toxins as they pass through the body. They also hydrate the body. All the cells, tissues and organs of the body require water to function optimally. Our bodies consist of at least 50% water and we lose some of that water throughout the day. A juice is a great way to replace lost body fluids. Carrots are loaded with beta-carotene and are low in calories. This is a great energy drink.

Handy hints: Cucumber does not only invigorate tired eyes, but a few slices of cucumber dabbed on your face help to moisturise your skin. Leave them on for about thirty minutes and then remove and rinse your face with cool water.

Ingredients
Makes 2 glasses

4 carrots
1cm ginger
1 table celery stalk with leaves
1 green apple, Granny Smith
½ cucumber, peeled
½ lemon + rind

Essentially, moderation teaches us to dispense with everything that may injure our health, while prudently using that which is healthful.

Green go-go

A dense green juice, rich in antioxidants with a definite garlicky taste. The apples and pears add a sweetness that makes it pleasant despite the garlic.

Ingredients
Makes 2 glasses

2 spinach/Swiss chard leaves
1 garlic clove
½ English cucumber
2 small green apples
2 small pears
A generous handful of parsley

'Living a healthy lifestyle will only deprive you of poor health, lethargy and fat.'
Jill Johnson

Benefits: This is a juice rich in B-complex vitamins, minerals and nutrients. Green apples are more commonly used for juicing. One reason is that they contain less sugar and more potassium than other apples do. Besides adding a daily dose of chlorophyll, spinach and parsley also provide support for those with iron-deficiency anaemia. This is a good green drink for muscle recovery. Greens always make good energy drinks.

Handy hints: A glass of pear juice will help to lower a fever. Drink a big glass when you feel a fever coming; it will build up your immune system.

Let's bounce

This is a good combination of greens to help us start off the day with energy or as a mid-afternoon juice to lift our fatigue.

Ingredients
Makes 2 glasses

2-4 spinach or kale leaves (remove the rib if you are using kale)
2 green apples
2cm ginger
1 stalk celery with leaves
3 broccoli florets
½ cucumber
Handful of parsley

Benefits: The effects of this juice are felt almost immediately as the nutrients, phytonutrients, minerals and vitamins pour into the bloodstream and take energy and oxygen into the cells. Spinach, celery, cucumber and apples are superfoods that are of great benefit to the cells. The anti-inflammatory properties of ginger help relieve joint and muscle pain.

Handy hints: People in many cultures have taken ginger to enhance their libido.

> 'More people die for want of exercise than through over-fatigue; very many more rust out than wear out.'
> *Ellen White*

Cabbage crush

Juiced cabbage has a surprisingly sweet taste. When combined with the citrus influence of lemon and the spicyness of cayenne, it makes for a wonderful flavour synergy.

Ingredients
Makes 2 glasses

¼ medium cabbage
1 spinach leaf
2 green apples
½ lemon
¼ tsp cayenne pepper

'Move a little more and eat a little less.'
Dr Alan Maryon Davies

It is estimated that 90% of obesity (with its diabetes consequences) could be abolished by walking an extra 2,000 steps and reducing calorie intake by a mere 100 calories a day!

Benefits: Cabbage is packed with vitamins and has impressive levels of calcium, iodine, iron, potassium, sulfur and phosphorus. It is thought that the phytochemicals in cabbage may help to defend the body against cancer-causing substances. Cayenne pepper and lemons are both reputed to aid in cleansing and detoxifying the body.

Handy hints: Place crushed cabbage leaves over painful, engorged breasts and let the leaf wither before replacing it. This is a natural remedy for relief during breast-feeding.

Sweet earth

Here the earthy taste of kale is combined with the sweetness of apple and pear juice. Add a piece of ginger for zing and mint for contrast and you have an unusual green juice. Pour over some ice and it is perfect for an afternoon energy lift.

Ingredients
Makes 2 glasses
2 pears
1 red apple
4 kale leaves
2cm ginger
Handful of parsley
Handful of mint

Benefits: This green juice is rich in vitamin B-complex nutrients, which are critical for all things mind-related, such as memory function, feelings and emotions. These vitamins are rich in antioxidants and anti-inflammatory properties. They are also thought to help diminish our risk of cancer. Vitamin B-complex nutrients are a key player in maintaining cell health and converting food into energy. Not all types of vitamin B do the same thing, however, and they all come from different types of foods. That is why variety in diet is important for our overall health.

Handy hints: Many of us don't get enough B-rich foods like green vegetables, wholegrains or animal proteins, especially of B6, B12 and folic acid.

'Those who think they have no time for bodily exercise will sooner or later have to find time for illness.'
Edward Stanley

Mike's basic green

Ingredients
Makes 1 glass

6 spinach leaves
60g cucumber
1 large Granny Smith
(green) apple

This is a good basic juice for someone who is starting to experiment with juicing. You may add any other green leafy vegetable or experiment with the addition of a sprig of fresh herbs, if you so wish.

Benefits: This juice is good for your skin and for normal eyesight because of all the nutrients and vitamins. Drinking it regularly will contribute to a radiant complexion. It is also a good drink for weight loss and the lowering of blood fats. Cucumber hydrates the system, thereby helping to cleanse the body of toxins. Apples contain no fat, sodium or cholesterol, and there are about 60-70 calories in a medium apple, which makes them a good fruit for weight maintenance. Apples are also a good source of fibre, which helps to cleanse and detoxify the body.

Handy hints: Did you know that apples can brighten and tighten your skin because of their high collagen and elastin content? These substances help to keep your skin youthful. So eat an apple every day!

'Reading is to
the mind what
exercise is to
the body.'
Joseph Addison

Clean green juice

This is a 'mean' juice. It clears my nasal passages almost immediately. It not only tastes healthy, but actually makes me feel healthier and more mentally alert. I think that the flavours blend well and I am sure you will enjoy it too.

Benefits: Apples, celery, cucumber, cabbage and lemon are all hydrating fruits and vegetables. All hydrating vegetables are good for detoxing too, so enjoy this drink at least once a week for a cleansing experience. You will also experience increased satiety levels. This makes it a good juice for weight loss and to improve the alkalinity of the digestive system.

Handy hints: Lemon juice helps block pain. When lemon juice is heated, salicylic acid, the active ingredient of aspirin, is produced.

Ingredients
Makes 2 glasses

2 green apples
2 celery stalks with leaves
½ English cucumber
2cm piece of ginger
⅛ of a cabbage
½ lemon, peeled

'Don't dig your grave with your own knife and fork!'
English proverb

Just green

Ingredients
Makes 1 glass

2 pears
1 green apple
2 celery stalks with
leaves
1 kiwi
10cm length of
cucumber
½ lemon, peeled

Everything in this juice except for the lemon is green. The combination of kiwi, green apple and lemon tingles the palate, leaving a fresh taste in your mouth. You could actually add another kiwi or two if you like the taste and won't suffer a reaction on your tongue.

Benefits: Kiwi fruit contains more vitamin C than an orange. I find it much easier to eat too. Juice it with the peel on but scrub as much of the hair off as possible first. Although the pear has a very high fibre content, it is also an easily digestible fruit, though the reasons for this are still unclear. It is an excellent fruit for the very young and the elderly. It helps mild constipation. Combine the pear and the celery and you have a good digestive system cleanser. The lemon must be one of the most versatile fruits. It helps to reduce pain and inflammation in joints and knees as it dissolves uric acid. Lemon is often used in remedies to alleviate the common cold.

Handy hints: Of particular interest to those who suffer from food allergies, the pear is often described as a 'hypoallergenic' (low-allergy) fruit.

'To be as fit as a fiddle, you must tone down your middle.'
Author unknown

Energise me

This juice really gets me up and going in the morning. It is a wonderful energiser. I actually like the taste of broccoli in a green juice, but am careful not to use too much because it does increase flatulence. Kale and parsley add a green earthiness to this drink that makes me know that I am drinking something from nature.

Benefits: Parsley is a highly nutritious herb, not a vegetable, although it is often used as a mere garnish. Nutritionally, I feel that it comes into its own when juiced. This tiny plant is rich in chlorophyll, vitamins, folate and iron, carotenoids and phytonutrients. Try adding a small handful to your daily green juice. Broccoli is one of those veggies that you either love or hate but it is a good source of protein and is also low in saturated fat and cholesterol. You can enjoy it raw or cooked.

Handy hints: If you would like a soup or sauce to have a parsley flavour but not a parsley colour, then you should only use the stems and not the green leaves.

Ingredients
Makes 1 glass

2 pears
4 kale leaves
½ English cucumber
1 carrot
3 broccoli florets
1 handful parsley
½ lemon with rind

'Use plant foods as the foundation of your meals. . . . Eating a variety of grains (especially wholegrains), fruits and vegetables is the basis of healthful eating.'
USDA Guidelines for Americans

Fill me up

Ingredients
Makes 2 glasses
Serve chilled.

2 celery stalks
½ medium sweet potato
4 carrots
4 kale leaves
4 spinach leaves
¼ lemon with skin
2 green apples

'Be sure to drink water that is pure and clean. It is the most healthfully beneficial liquid we can consume.'
Kathleen Kuntaraf

This is a surprisingly filling juice with a distinct tuber taste. The addition of sweet potato adds to the feeling of satiety you will have after drinking it. This juice could easily be enjoyed as a meal replacement. Sweet potato leaves a residue at the bottom of the glass so remember to stir well before drinking.

Benefits: The humble carrot is an excellent source of beta-carotene. It is low on calories, a weight watcher's dream veggie. Kale and spinach create an intense green veggie taste combination which is relieved by the addition of carrot, apple and lemon. Kale is thought to ease lung congestion and is beneficial to the stomach, liver and immune system. Celery, carrot, kale, lemon and spinach are superfoods which possess above-normal beneficial properties.

Handy hints: Apples contain no fat, sodium or cholesterol, and are a good source of fibre. An apple a day could keep your doctor away.

Sweet cucumber

A very filling juice because of the water content of the cucumber, but the use of cucumber also makes it light. Be aware, though, that cucumber is a natural diuretic. Apples add a balancing sweetness to this juice and the mint completes the taste.

Ingredients
Makes 2 small glasses

4 handfuls of spinach
2 cucumbers
2 red apples
¼ cup of mint leaves

Benefits: Spinach is one of the top leafy vegetables for juicing. It is loaded with vitamins, minerals and nutrients. These include vitamin A, vitamin B-complex, vitamin C, vitamin K, manganese, folate, iron, calcium, potassium, tryptophan, vitamin E, copper, protein and zinc. Cucumber is wonderful for digestion because it contains lots of water and fibre, which serve to hydrate and cleanse the body. But cucumber is not only good for the inside of the body, because the magnesium, potassium and silicon it contains make it a popular ingredient in many cosmetic preparations for use on the outside of the body too.

Handy hints: Placing slices of cucumber on the eyes really does reduce under-eye bags and puffiness, helping to revive the beauty of your eyes. It only takes 20 minutes. Massaging your face with slices of cucumber also soothes and moisturises it. Leave it on for about 30 minutes and then wash it off with warm water.

'A cheerful heart is good medicine.'
Proverbs 17:22, NIV

Minty pineapple

Ingredients
Makes 2 glasses

1 cucumber
2 red apples
1 cup pineapple
2 cups tightly pressed
kale leaves
¼ cup mint
½ peeled lemon
3 ice cubes per glass

'Happiness cannot
be travelled to,
owned, earned,
worn or consumed.
Happiness is
the spiritual
experience of living
every minute with
love, grace and
gratitude.'
Denis Waitle

I love a juicy sweet pineapple with just a tinge of tang to it. Although this is a green juice it has a minty pineapple taste which is quite delightful. Serve it chilled with a few fresh mint leaves.

Benefits: Kale is packed with vitamins that include beta-carotene (which the body converts into vitamin A), vitamin C, vitamin B6 and vitamin K, along with quite a few minerals. All of these will be an obvious benefit to one's health. There are different kale varieties and it doesn't matter which one you use for juicing. Pineapple is known for the alkaline substance bromelain, which aids in digestion and is linked to a reduction of inflammation in arthritis and other inflammatory disorders. Mint not only flavours this juice but it is also nutrient-rich and an excellent diuretic.

Handy hints: Pineapple juice is potent. Mixed with sand it's apparently an amazing cleaning agent for things as varied as boat decks and knife blades. I haven't tried this though.

Green love

The apples and broccoli give this juice a lovely sweet taste. Apple juice blends well with other vegetable juices, which makes it a natural choice as a sweetener for a green juice. The sodium in the celery gives it a pleasantly salty taste.

Benefits: Apples contain vitamins, minerals and malic acid, which have detoxification benefits, aid digestion, help lower cholesterol and improve the condition of one's skin. There are so many varieties of apples to choose from and they are all good for you. Spinach is one of the top leafy vegetables for juicing and supplies an impressive array of vitamins, minerals and nutrients. Cucumbers are wonderful for digestion because they contain lots of water and fibre, which serve to hydrate and cleanse the body. Lemon alkalises the body and boosts our resilience.

Handy hints: Celery does contain sodium, but it is a good salt, not the same thing as table salt. It is organic, natural and essential for your health.

Ingredients
Makes 2 glasses

2 cups spinach
1 cup broccoli with stalks
3 celery stalks
1 cucumber
½ lemon
2 apples

People really do need people, and are generally healthier with their family around them.

Winter green

Ingredients
Makes 2 glasses

2 celery stalks
4 spinach leaves
4 broccoli florets
2 large carrots
3 Granny Smith apples
A chunk of ginger
(according to your
taste)
1 garlic clove
¼ cup fresh coriander

'Health is
the greatest
possession.
Contentment is the
greatest treasure.
Confidence is the
greatest friend.'
Lao Tzu

This is a juice for when the seasons change or when your immune system is in distress. All its nutrients and vitamins work together to help clear your system and make you feel 'chin up' for the day.

Benefits: I know that celery tastes like water, but that's because it has a high water content. Celery also contains insoluble fibre, which, when combined with a high water content, makes it a wonderful vegetable for those who suffer from constipation. For those who suffer from various joint problems, celery reduces inflammation and also helps to alkalise the body. It is commonly accepted that celery is a good choice for weight watchers because one stalk only contains about 10 calories and the high water content fills you up quickly. So celery is definitely a good food choice.

Handy hints: The high water content and the insoluble fibre present in celery make it a great choice for those who suffer from constipation, but it should be avoided by those suffering with diarrhoea.

No limits

One can really experiment when making fresh juices. You are only limited by your own personal preferences and sense of adventure. I like going into my little garden in the morning and gathering my own collection of green leaves for my morning juice, then adding some apple, lemon, ginger, carrot . . . and I'm good to go!

Benefits: Baby leaves are very tender and less pungent. They blend easily into this juice, combining flavour with the nutrients and minerals that our bodies need. I prefer this juice in the morning as a meal because it cleanses, energises, detoxes, hydrates and fills you up. Heavy metals such as mercury, lead and aluminium can accumulate in the body over time. Coriander is one of the herbs known for ridding the body of such substances. But this popular herb also has other beneficial properties, like supporting cardiovascular health and contributing towards the lowering of blood sugar.

Handy hints: In the UK 'coriander' refers to the plant's leaves, while the seeds are called 'coriander seeds'. In the US the plant is called 'cilantro' and the seeds are called 'coriander'.

Ingredients
Makes 1 glass

1 cucumber
2 celery stalks without leaves
½ cup of coriander leaves (cilantro)
3 cups mixed baby leaves (spinach, beetroot, kale, cauliflower, etc)
1 large carrot
2 apples
2cm piece of ginger
½ small lemon

'To ensure good health: eat lightly, breathe deeply, live moderately, cultivate cheerfulness, and maintain an interest in life.'
William Londen

Green peace

Ingredients
Makes 2 glasses

1 cucumber
3 celery stalks
3 big spinach leaves
1 red bell pepper
2 red apples
½ grapefruit
Small handful of
parsley

A refreshing sweet green juice with a hint of citrus. The flavour of red pepper is less pungent in this juice than that of a green pepper.

Benefits: Cucumber and celery are great natural diuretics and help flush out toxins as they pass through the body. They also hydrate the body, something all the cells, tissues and organs of the body require to function optimally. We lose some of that water throughout the day and this juice is a great way to replace those lost fluids. Spinach is one of the top leafy vegetables for juicing. It is loaded with vitamins, minerals and nutrients. Grapefruit is rich in potassium, which helps to smooth wrinkles, fade age spots and provide some protection against the harmful rays of the sun. Red bell peppers are a great source of vitamin B6 and magnesium. Some sources suggest that this vitamin-and-mineral combination contributes to a decrease in anxiety. In addition to which, one cup will give you more than your daily quota of vitamins A and C.

Handy hints: Bell peppers are an excellent weight-loss food because they are so low in calories, with only about 45 to a cup!

'A good laugh and a long sleep are the best cures in the doctor's book.'
Irish proverb

Orange green

A lovely morning drink, filling and satisfying. I love eating an orange as a quick energy fix. It must be at room temperature so that the juice is warm and sweet in my mouth. But you might like to serve this juice over some ice cubes with a crushed lemon leaf in the glass.

Benefits: Oranges have a wealth of nutrients, including vitamin C, vitamin A, calcium, potassium, and pectin. They are a quick snack for anyone on the run. Apples are a rich source of dietary fibre and vitamin C and they both soothe the digestive system and provide energy. Spinach is one of the top leafy vegetables for juicing as it is regarded to have anti-inflammatory properties and generally helps the body fight disease. Besides adding a daily dose of chlorophyll, spinach also provides support for iron-deficiency anaemia. Celery adds natural sodium to this drink and is also a great natural diuretic, helping to rid the body of toxins. For those who suffer from various joint problems, celery is thought to reduce inflammation and, like oranges and lemons, it helps to alkalise the body.

Handy hints: Rolling an orange under the palm of your hand on a flat surface will help to release more juice.

Ingredients
Makes 1 glass

½ cucumber
4 large celery stalks
1 cup baby spinach
2 peeled oranges
½ lemon including the skin
1 green apple

'Physical fitness is not only one of the most important keys to a healthy body: it is the basis of dynamic and creative intellectual activity.'
John F. Kennedy

Just a green juice

Ingredients
Makes 2 glasses

2 celery stalks
½ cucumber
1 cup baby spinach
1 cup baby kale leaves
1 medium beetroot
without leaves
2 green pears
1 green apple
Small handful parsley
½ lemon

This green juice is richly coloured and flavoured. I've added just one beetroot and it's amazing how this enhances the taste of everything else.

Benefits: Green juices are rich in vitamin B-complex nutrients, which are critical for memory function, feelings and emotions. Green juices are rich in antioxidants and have anti-inflammatory properties. The baby leaves are not as pungent as mature leaves and blend well with the pear and apple. Both cucumber and celery are water-rich vegetables, helping to replace any electrolytes which are lost during exercising. They also help to keep the kidneys working well. Beetroot juice has become a firm favourite with athletes for sustained energy. Beetroots are rich in folic acid and manganese and are often used to help combat anaemia, improve lymphatic circulation and reduce tiredness. They are among the iron-rich foods and help to improve the quality of the blood.

Handy hints: Gremolata is a wonderful fresh Italian garnish that can be quickly prepared for use as a great sprinkle: finely chopped parsley (about 2 tablespoons), half a clove of garlic and zest from a lemon. Add at the last minute so that the aroma is still there when you serve your dish.

'So whether you eat or drink or whatever you do, do it all for the glory of God.'
1 Corinthians 10:31, NIV

Apple-kiwi mint

A nice light drink, in which the flavours blend well together and to which the lemongrass adds an exotic lemon tinge.

Benefits: Apples are well known for their many health benefits. There are many different varieties to choose from and they are all good for us. An apple a day is definitely a great way to keep the doctor away, as the old saying goes. Kiwi fruit grows on a vine and, although associated with New Zealand, it is now grown more widely. This green and juicy fruit contains more vitamin C than an orange and has a slightly tart taste. Juice it with the skin on but scrub as much of the hair as possible off first. Ginger contains anti-inflammatory properties that are reputed to relieve joint and muscle pain. Lemongrass is a natural remedy used to treat coughs, colds and fever.

Handy hints: Lemons should be picked when they have reached their 'peak ripeness' because they do not ripen or improve in nutritional quality after this point. Take care, though, not to drink large quantities of pure lemon juice because of its damaging effect on our teeth.

Ingredients
Makes 2 glasses

2 green apples
3 kiwis
1 large cucumber
2cm chunk of ginger
1 lemongrass stalk, peeled

'If we're not willing to settle for junk living, we certainly shouldn't settle for junk food.'
Sally Edwards

Freshly green

Ingredients
Makes 2 glasses

3 cups spinach
1 cup broccoli florets
1 cup fresh pineapple
3 celery stalks
2 red apples
½ cucumber
½ lemon

'It's difficult to think anything but pleasant thoughts while eating a homegrown tomato.'
Lewis Grizzard

Some mornings I like a rather substantial drink – some goodness in a glass. This juice is packed with all the necessary vitamins and nutrients that I need for the day, and I love the sweetness that the broccoli, pineapple and apple provide.

Benefits: The effects of this juice appear to be quite rapid as the nutrients, phytonutrients, minerals and vitamins pour into the bloodstream and take energy and oxygen into the cells. Spinach, celery, cucumber and apples are 'superfoods' that promote optimum health. They hydrate the body and help to remove harmful toxins. Pineapple is also a good cleanser, especially when you've overindulged.

Handy hints: 'Superfoods' are those considered to be nutrient-rich and especially beneficial for health and well-being.

Energy juices

It is commonly accepted that, when juicing for energy, vegetable-based recipes will generally deliver more of what we are looking for. In addition to that, just remember that your 'green' juices are the ones most likely to give you a quick boost of energy.

This is your opportunity to think outside the traditional 'veggie' rack and use some of those easily neglected ingredients that are actually packed with 'green' energy. Parsley is one that springs to mind, but there are others too. One that has emerged as a frontrunner recently is wheatgrass, an excellent energy-packed, nutrient-rich grass that is grown from wheat berry seeds – something you can do in your backyard. Owing to its high concentration of chlorophyll its juice has a bright green colour.

At this point we should bear in mind that persistent feelings of fatigue may need more than a series of energy-filled juices to correct. We also need to ensure that the other important elements of a balanced and healthy lifestyle are in place: enough quality sleep; sufficient daily physical activity to keep one in good health; and a balanced, healthy diet.

Should these efforts not rectify the situation, make sure that you consult your doctor.

Iron booster

The combination of beetroot, carrot and apple is often referred to as the 'miracle drink' because of the wonderful nutrients and vitamins that they give you. This juice is especially good when you feel exhausted.

Benefits: Beetroot is of great nutritional value, being particularly rich in folic acid and manganese, which is helpful in relieving conditions like anaemia, poor lymphatic circulation and tiredness. This iron-rich vegetable is also good for detoxing the liver. One of the major benefits of beetroot juice is that it contains a colour pigment called betalain, which has powerful antioxidant, anti-inflammatory and fungicidal properties. It is best to have beetroot juice raw because most of the beneficial substances, like betalain, are lost when cooked.

Handy hints: Beetroot juice causes both your stools and urine to turn red. Don't be surprised if this happens; it is due to the colour pigment betalain.

Ingredients
Makes 1 glass

2 large beetroots
2 carrots
1 Granny Smith apple
1 cup spinach
½ lemon

'He gives strength to those who are tired and more power to those who are weak.'
Isaiah 40:29, NCV

Berry C

Ingredients
Makes 1 glass

1 cup blackberries
1 cup strawberries
2 peeled oranges
2 kiwi fruit
½ tsp lemon juice

An excellent vitamin C booster juice with a distinct citrus berry flavour that is very pleasant. This juice is quite filling and provides lots of energy.

Benefits: Berries are packed with antioxidants, chemicals that can prevent or slow down cell damage. By adding antioxidant-rich fruits and vegetables to your daily diet you will strengthen your body's ability to fight infection and disease. Besides the fact that all citrus fruits are great energy providers, they also contain many healing phytonutrients. An added bonus is that they have a low glycaemic index, which means that you can have them in moderation and not fear a spike in your blood sugar. All these fruits are high in vitamin C, which is essential for maintaining and repairing our immune systems. The pH level in our bodies is very important. When our bodies are more acidic, they become more prone to disease and infection. Certain foods assist us in keeping our bodies more alkaline, and lemon, though acidic, is one of the best foods for making our blood alkaline.

Handy hints: Having a glass of warm lemon water every morning before breakfast aids digestion, improves the alkalinity of the body, helps to clear up bad skin, and helps to clear out the toxins and keep you regular.

'A recipe has no soul. You, as the cook, must bring soul to the recipe.'
Thomas Keller

Sunrise simplicity

This is probably one of the most common juices and is a favourite with most people. It took a while for me to experiment and find the proportions that I like, and I would recommend that you do the same. I like to enjoy this as a morning juice before I go for my run.

Ingredients
Makes 1 glass

4 large carrots
2 Granny Smith apples
1 chunk ginger

Benefits: Carrots are perhaps best known for their rich supply of the antioxidant nutrient that was actually named for them, beta-carotene. All varieties of carrots contain the antioxidant vitamin C, as well as phytonutrient antioxidants like beta-carotene. Beta-carotene has also been shown to protect against macular degeneration and senile cataracts. The health benefits of carrots include the improvement of eyesight, slowing down the ageing process, helping prevent cancer and the protection of teeth and gums. Ginger is so concentrated with active substances, you don't have to use very much to receive its beneficial effects.

Handy hints: For nausea, make a ginger tea by steeping one or two slices of fresh ginger in a cup of hot water for five minutes. This will very likely settle your stomach.

'Cookery is not chemistry. It is an art. It requires instinct and taste rather than exact measurements.'
Marcel Boulestin

Energy boost

Ingredients
Makes 1 glass

2 cups baby kale leaves
1-2 cups green seedless grapes
½ cucumber
1 Granny Smith apple
1 small pear
1cm chunk ginger
½ lemon

'Let food be thy medicine and medicine be thy food.'
Hippocrates

This juice provides a quick afternoon energy restorer when your strength is flagging.

Benefits: Kale is packed with vitamins and these nutritional properties have been shown to lower our risk of developing quite a few types of cancer. There are different kale varieties and it doesn't matter which one you use for juicing. Grape juice provides iron to the body and this helps to prevent fatigue. Iron carries oxygen from our lungs to the rest of our cells and helps our muscles use and store oxygen. Too little iron in the body makes one anaemic, and eating grapes can help keep up our iron and mineral levels. A lack of iron can make you sluggish. Ginger is good for nausea, cramps and flatulence. A ginger tea, with or without lemon and honey, helps protect the body against colds.

Handy hints: Grapes are a good laxative food and a natural remedy for constipation. Having a bunch of grapes daily will help to keep you regular.

Homemade grape juice

A simple glass of grape juice provides an almost instant energy boost. I remember my grandmother pressing grapes for the quarterly Communion Service (Lord's Supper) at our church and allowing me to taste the finished product. In my memory it was the best-tasting juice.

Ingredients
Makes 1 glass

4 cups grapes
1 green apple

Benefits: Grapes are filled with many antioxidant phytonutrients and nutrients. But the richest concentration of antioxidants is in the seeds and the skin of the grape. So don't discard the skins as you eat them. Grapes have many health benefits; the most well-known is probably its support of cardiovascular health. But grapes are also beneficial to other systems and organs of the body. Grapes contain powerful antioxidants known as polyphenols, which are thought to protect the body against many types of cancer.

Grapes contain a lot of water and this helps to keep the body hydrated, and, combined with the fibre content, to keep bowel movements regular. One cup of grapes is a quick 100-calorie energy snack and would also count as one of your fruits for the day. The antioxidants in grapes also serve a cosmetic purpose. Fruits that are rich in antioxidants are thought to help you fight wrinkles, age spots and other signs of ageing.

Handy hints: I love this hint and I think that you would too. Freeze some grapes and add them to your morning smoothie or eat them as a snack or dessert on a hot day. Children will love them too.

'A heart at peace gives life to the body, but envy rots the bones.'
Proverbs 14:30, NIV

Celery and apple

Ingredients
Makes 1 glass

3 green apples
6 celery stalks (without leaves)

This is a light, fragrant juice with a slightly salty taste that comes from the sodium in the celery. It is very satisfying and sustaining, especially through a workout. Juiced celery is nothing like eating fresh celery: even the pickiest eater should enjoy it. Serve immediately.

Benefits: Apple juice helps to cleanse your digestive system and is a good addition in a detox programme. Apples will enhance the taste of almost any fruit or vegetable drink without clashing with the other flavours. They contain at least 5% soluble fibre, which means that eating an apple makes you feel full for longer. Soluble fibre takes a longer time to pass through our bodies, and during that time it makes our tummies feel full. An apple is low in calories and has no fat, so it is a weight-watcher's dream fruit.

Celery has a salty taste and so mixes very well with a sweet fruit like an apple. It is also nutrient-rich and has many health benefits, including its ability to balance the body's blood pH and keep it alkaline. One interesting fact about celery is that – unlike many other vegetables – it does not lose too many of its nutrients during cooking.

Handy hints: If you are storing fresh celery in a refrigerator, do not store it for longer than 5-7 days. This will ensure that you enjoy the maximum nutritional benefit.

'No one who cooks, cooks alone. Even at her most solitary, a cook in the kitchen is surrounded by generations of cooks past, the advice and menus of cooks present, the wisdom of cookbook writers.'
Laurie Colwin

Simple sweet potato

This juice came to me from the Caymans. I tried this juice recipe on a group of unsuspecting friends at a long weekend get-together. When I said it was simply sweet potato and apple – there was a resounding, 'Really?' Try it yourself and prepare to be surprised. Enjoy it! I did!

Ingredients
Makes 2 glasses

2 sweet potatoes
1 Pink Lady apple
Fine cinnamon for sprinkling

Benefits: There are many different types of sweet potatoes. I've used orange ones, but Edeona (who gave me the recipe) used pink sweet potatoes. Sweet potato is a complex carb that provides a slow release of energy to keep us going over a longer period of time, especially when we need energy for exercise. Sweet potatoes have a very low glycaemic loading and are a good alternative to Irish or white potatoes for those who have to watch their blood sugar levels. The glycaemic index indicates how a particular food affects your blood sugar levels. For instance, if you are diabetic you will want to avoid having food with a high glycaemic index that would push up your blood sugar levels. Sweet potato has a bit of an earthy taste that is beautifully complimented by the Pink Lady apple. I tried the Granny Smith apple in this recipe and it was also good.

One of the benefits of cinnamon, apart from its wonderfully spicy aroma, is that it is loaded with antioxidants that protect the body from destructive free radicals.

Handy hints: If you want to begin a vegetable patch and don't know what to begin with, sweet potato makes a good beginner's garden crop. It only requires 100 frost-free days in order to grow.

'The preparation of good food is merely another expression of art, one of the joys of civilised living . . .'
Dione Lucas

Orange and carrot

Ingredients
Makes 2 glasses

4 oranges
4 large carrots
½ cup mint leaves
3 ice cubes per glass

Oranges and carrots are such simple and well-known foods, but really a rare treat when combined in a juice. The sweetness of the carrots and the tart citrus flavour of the orange make for a perfect winter morning drink. This juice can easily pass as a meal.

Benefits: I remember being an athletics marshal and handing out orange wedges to runners. Even a wedge of orange was considered sufficient for a burst of energy release for the runner. It is probably common knowledge that the orange is a good source of vitamin C, but we might not know why that is important. Vitamin C protects the body from free radicals, which can damage one's health in many ways, including inflammatory conditions such as arthritis.

Among other benefits, carrots help to protect our vision. They contain complex carbs that slowly release energy. Mint is known to calm stomach cramps and help beat acidity and flatulence, but it also adds a freshness to any dish – this juice is no exception.

Handy hints: If you are feeling low, add a few mint leaves or mint extract to your bath water. Mint helps to relax the body and calm the mind.

'Nothing tends to promote health of body and soul than does a spirit of thankfulness and praise. It is a positive duty to resist melancholy, discontented thoughts and feelings.'
Ellen White

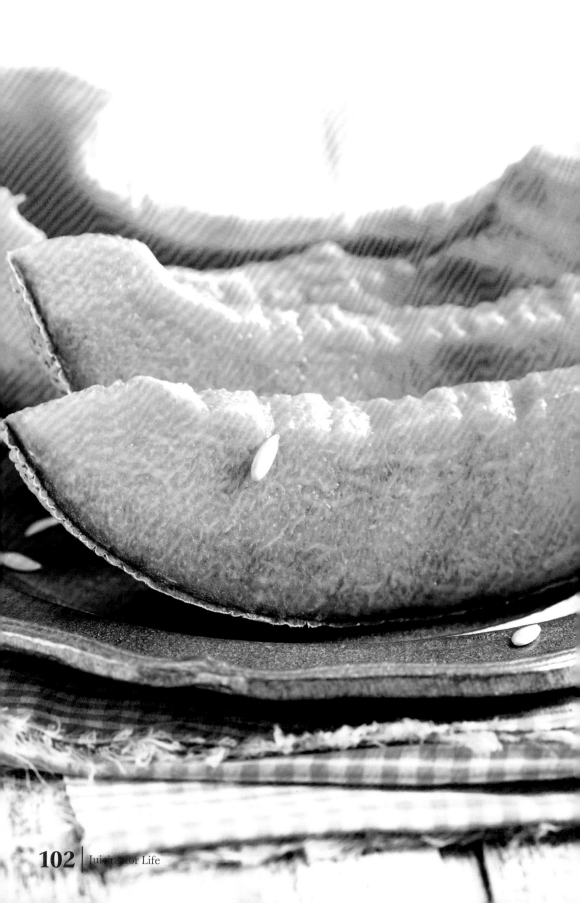

Melon morning

This recipe produces a sweet, gentle-tasting juice which is surprisingly unaffected by the inclusion of spinach. Serve over crushed ice with a sprig of mint or a slice of lime. The colour is wonderful too.

Ingredients
Makes 2 glasses

½ sweet melon/
cantaloupe
2 green apples
1 handful baby spinach
leaves
Crushed ice for each
glass

Benefits: Sweet melons are a wonderful source of beta-carotene and folic acid. Besides being a good cleanser, melon juice also provides a quick release of energy. Apples are a rich source of dietary fibre and vitamin C. They also soothe the digestive system. Apples have a natural sugar that produces acids to stimulate digestion and provide energy. Spinach is one of the top leafy vegetables for juicing and it is full of health benefits.

Handy hints: How do you check whether a melon is ripe? It should be very fragrant and heavy. If you press the end opposite the stem there should be a bit of give. Tap the melon, and you'll hear a hollow sound if it's ripe.

'To eat is a necessity, but to eat intelligently is an art.'
François de La Rochefoucauld

Ruby red

Ingredients
Makes 1 glass

1 beetroot
1 apple
1 celery heart
1cm chunk ginger
2 tbsp chia seeds
(soaked for 15
minutes)

Beetroot is amazingly sweet when juiced. It should be juiced raw but cooked for use in a smoothie. I am always surprised at how much liquid I get from one beetroot. Although it could be an acquired taste for some, beetroot is coming into its own as an energy-boosting drink.

Benefits: One cup of raw beetroot has 58 calories and 13 grams of carbohydrates. A cup of beetroot juice usually contains around 100 calories and 25 grams of carbohydrates. Beetroot is very useful in fighting anaemia and its juice is being touted as the new wonder juice – ideal for athletes and those involved in workouts that require stamina.

Chia seeds become plump and sweet when they are soaked in liquid, expanding up to fifteen times their original size. They also have more antioxidants than most berries, as well as fibre, protein, calcium and omega-3s.

Handy hints: While many foods lose nutrients during cooking, most of the compounds in celery hold up well during cooking.

'Sorry, there's no magic bullet. You gotta eat healthy and live healthy to be healthy and look healthy. End of story.'
Morgan Spurlock

Juices for weight loss

While juicing may help with some weight loss and weight maintenance, it is important to remember that it is unlikely to be the average dieter's 'magic bullet'. This is due to the fact that whether we are using fruit or vegetables to create our juices, or a combination of both, they all contain some calories.

Juicing separates the calorie-dense juice from the fruit or veggie's fibre – what we normally refer to as pulp. The juice of most fruits contains much more sugar than many of us realise. For example, very few of us would eat four normal-sized oranges at one sitting, but that is effectively what we do when we consume one standard glass (250ml) of orange juice. Most orange juices contain 10g of sugar per 100ml. That totals 25g of sugar just from the oranges alone – more than you'll get from a 39g Cadbury Wispa bar (20.5g)!

So, when juicing for either weight loss or weight maintenance, we need to make sure our juices are really effective by following this rule of thumb: let vegetables form the bulk of our ingredients!

Sources: *http://www.telegraph.co.uk/news/health/children/11130095/The-10-fruit-juices-with-more-sugar-than-Coca-Cola.html* and *http://www.tesco.com/groceries/product/details/?id=263218070*

Anytimer

This makes quite a large quantity of juice that is sweet, tangy and refreshing. Depending on how you like it, you can either cut back on the apple, add an extra apple or use different kinds of apples together to vary the taste. There is just enough ginger in it to give you an obvious hit without dominating the drink.

Benefits: As we have already mentioned, cucumber is a natural diuretic and helps to cleanse our systems of toxins. It also reduces water retention. Cucumber is rich in silica to nourish your hair, skin and nails. Celery also helps to remove excess water from your body, even though it is itself a water-rich vegetable. Celery adds a salty taste to this juice. It also helps to nourish the body.

Handy hints: A ginger tea, with or without lemon and honey, protects the body against colds. Steep slices of ginger in hot water for 5 minutes and sip.

Ingredients
Makes 2 large glasses

2 apples
1 cucumber
4 large celery stalks
2-3cm chunk ginger
6 kale/spinach leaves
½ a lemon

'Lack of activity destroys the good condition of every human being, while movement and methodical physical exercise save it and preserve it.'
Plato

Green queen

Ingredients
Makes 2 glasses

2 cups kale
3 celery stalks with leaves
1 cucumber
½-1 lemon
2 Fuji or Pink Lady apples

'Dear friend, I pray that you may enjoy good health and that all may go well with you, just as you are progressing spiritually.'
3 John 1:2, NIV-UK

When you are juicing for weight loss always use more veggies than fruit because of the natural sugar in fruit. If you are trying to gain weight then you can use more fruit than veggies. This juice is very similar to the previous one, except for the ginger kick. Sometimes you may want a green juice without the ginger.

Benefits: The effect of this juice is felt almost immediately as the nutrients, phytonutrients, minerals and vitamins pour into the bloodstream, taking energy and oxygen into the cells. Spinach, celery, cucumber and apples are 'superfoods' that bring potential healing to the cells while simultaneously cleansing the body of toxins.

Handy hints: Including lemon water in your daily health regimen is reputed to reduce joint inflammation as it dissolves uric acid.

Spicy green

This green juice is not only good for weight loss, but also for detoxing after those overindulgent days when your system feels clogged up. You can adjust the fruit and veggie amounts to suit your personal taste. You will find celery adding a bit of a salty taste, which contrasts beautifully with the sweeter apple. Ginger and cayenne give this juice a spicy twist. Enjoy!

Ingredients
Makes 2 glasses

2 apples
4 celery stalks
1 cucumber
6 kale leaves
½ lemon
2cm fresh ginger
Good pinch of cayenne

Benefits: Apples contain a fair amount of dietary fibre that cleanses the body. They also have a natural sugar that produces acids to stimulate digestion. The fibre in an apple helps to lower cholesterol. For those of us who are past the flush of youth, apples contain vitamins A and C, which help prevent sagging skin, as well as copper for brightening and toning the skin. Celery contains natural, safe sodium, which has been called a youth maintainer in the body. It's rich in minerals and nutrients, especially vitamin C, which helps maintain the elasticity of the skin. The surprising thing about kale is that, although it is loaded with good things, it is not an overpowering taste. I love the spicy zing that ginger and cayenne pepper give this juice.

Handy hints: Through many civilisations and over many centuries ginger has been used as an aphrodisiac.

'You are what you eat. What would *you* like to be?'
Julie Murphy

Beet it

Ingredients
Makes 2 glasses

2 beetroots
2 large carrots
2 oranges
1 cup spinach
½ medium pineapple
½-1 lemon to taste

Beetroot has powerful pigments that will turn any juice red, an intense red, and it is surprisingly sweet. This is quite a filling juice and helpful when one juices to lose weight. Please give it a try; it is delicious.

Benefits: Beetroot juice has become a popular energy source among athletes because the carbs in beetroot give instant energy. Beetroot is known to be particularly good at cleansing the liver of toxicity and stimulating bile functions. It is also an excellent source of vitamin C, which helps to protect the immune system. Carrots are rich in carotenoids, which help to regulate blood sugar and reduce the risk of heart disease. Carrots also contain complex carbs that give the body energy and keep you feeling full for longer. Carrots also protect our eyes against disease. Lemons and oranges help to control high blood pressure, but they also provide energy and a feeling of satiety.

Handy hints: The choline from beetroot juice not only detoxifies the liver, but can also help the body recover from excessive alcohol abuse.

'Simple, natural food is far better than sophisticated food with artificial flavours.'
Dr Sivakumar Gowder

Oranges and lemons

Its citrus and faint ginger flavour makes this juice delightful. Serve over ice cubes.

Ingredients
Makes 2 glasses

3 apples
3 large celery stalks
1 cucumber
2cm ginger
4 kale leaves
1 lemon
1 orange

Benefits: Cucumber contains silica, which is essential for the areas where you find connective tissue, especially our muscles, bones, cartilage, ligaments and tendons. It is commonly used in cosmetics because the silicon is good for the health of the skin. Cucumber also hydrates the body and the skin due to its high water content. Celery contains natural sodium, which has been called a youth maintainer in the body. It's loaded with minerals and contains vitamin C as well, which helps maintain elasticity of the skin. There are elements in all of these ingredients that contribute to preserving the health and youthfulness of the skin. The benefits of this juice include helping to maintain a healthy blood pressure, calorie control and weight loss, and assisting the body to fight cancer and respiratory problems.

Handy hints: Apparently (I haven't tried this yet) oranges will produce more juice when warmer. So always juice them when they are at room temperature.

'I don't confuse my digestive system; I just season simple food with hunger.'
Richard Proenneke

The body scrubber

Ingredients
Makes 2 glasses

1 apple
1 beetroot
8 large carrots
2 large stalks celery
2 cups spinach

'The food you eat can be either the safest and most powerful form of medicine or the slowest form of poison.'
Ann Wigmore

What is wonderful about this juice is that all the ingredients combine to cleanse various parts of the body and the apple juice acts as a gentle laxative. You can serve this over a couple of ice cubes.

Benefits: Beetroot and spinach both help to improve the quality of our blood because of their high iron content. Beetroot juice has recently become a popular juice among athletes, but drinking beetroot juice regularly will also help relieve chronic constipation. Beetroot and carrots are also known liver cleansers. Carrots are rich in beta-carotene, which is regarded as having valuable antioxidant properties that are able to protect the body against inflammation. Carrots also help to cleanse the blood and regulate blood sugar, and we all know that carrots protect the eyes against degeneration. Apparently eating apples regularly will also improve the intestinal tract's ability to process body waste. Celery and apples are loaded with minerals and vitamins that are excellent for maintaining the elasticity of the skin, as well as copper for brightening and toning.

Handy hints: Celery is a high-sodium whole food. It is one of a few vegetables, like beetroot and carrots, that you can easily use to replace processed salt in your cooking. One large stalk of celery has about 50mg of sodium.

Cabbage cleanser

I know that most people would consider cabbage to be a potent ingredient in a juice: it is. But I've found cabbage to be surprisingly sweet when juiced and not at all as potent as I had expected it to be. Surprise, surprise!

Benefits: Cabbage belongs to the cruciferous clan and as such shares its rich phytonutrients that can contribute to weight loss. These phytonutrients contribute to the health of the body in many ways, including the improvement of your metabolism. Metabolism is the process by which our bodies convert what we eat and drink into energy, which means that it is vital to have a good metabolism. These phytonutrients also assist with flushing out toxins, reducing inflammation and helping with body fat maintenance. Apples are a gentle laxative and help to cleanse the body, especially the subcutaneous layers where the body stores its fat. Cucumber and celery are both natural diuretics and celery helps to fight water retention by helping to remove all the excess fluid in your body.

Handy hints: Carrots and celery form the basis of many an excellent stock because they are naturally high in sodium and reduce the need for large quantities of salt during cooking.

Ingredients
Makes 2 glasses

¼ cabbage
2 green apples
½ cucumber
4 carrots
4 stalks celery
Pinch of cayenne

'Malnutrition can be as common in poverty as in wealth: one for the lack of food, the other for the lack of knowledge of food.'
T. K. Naliaka

Grapefruit flush

Ingredients
Makes 1 glass

½ grapefruit
2 green apples
4 large celery ribs

I have to confess that I've only recently been won over to the taste of grapefruit in a juice. It is pungent, especially if you have added the peel, but very satisfying. Keep your grapefruit juices simple with as few ingredients as possible so that the grapefruit flavour is clearly distinguishable. This is a great fat-burning energy juice.

Benefits: You either love or hate grapefruit but it is a taste that can't be ignored. Like all citrus fruits it is a great cleanser. Grapefruit has long been known as an excellent food for weight loss as it seems to naturally boost our metabolism. But it is known as a 'negative-calorie' food because of exaggerated claims it can take more energy to digest than it supplies. It is also full of fibre, which keeps you feeling full. Celery helps to rid the body of excess fluid while at the same time nourishing and restoring the body with much-needed nutrients, vitamins and minerals. Including apple in a juice increases the elimination of toxins from the body. Apples are high in soluble fibre, which helps to soothe digestion.

Handy hints: Weight loss requires more than just a couple of good juices, and you cannot live on juice alone. An increase in your daily physical exercise routine can vastly improve your chances of burning more calories each day.

'Variety in your diet is health in your life.'
Toni Sorenson

Pineapple pleaser

Enjoying a juice based on pineapple will provide the body with that little bit of sweetness that we sometimes crave without the pileup of calories in the body. A couple of slices of fresh pineapple contain fewer calories and more vitamin C than a slice of cake. Adding a bit of lemon to your juice always improves the flavour.

Benefits: It is wonderful that pineapples are low in calories, while also being rich in antioxidants, especially vitamin C, which helps protect your immune system against colds and flu. Pineapples are also high in fibre and water, making them the perfect snack to stave off those hunger pangs. Foods with a high water content make you feel full for longer and that helps to curb your appetite, which of course is essential for weight loss. The liver is one of the most important organs of the body. Functions that are important for weight loss, like metabolism, detoxification, and the regulation of blood glucose levels, all take place here. The valuable nutrients in broccoli also contribute to the health of the liver. Celery helps to rid the body of excess fluid and then it helps to nourish the body. Pears, like lemons, reduce the acidity in the body.

Handy hints: Lemon juice helps to maintain the alkalinity of the body. Germs and diseases flourish in an acidic environment.

Ingredients
Makes 2 glasses

2 small peeled pineapples
2 firm pears
2 celery stalks
1 cup broccoli
½ lemon

'Maybe your mind won't remember what I cooked last week, but your body will.'
Erica Bauermeister

Basic combo

Ingredients
Makes 2 glasses

5 carrots
1 cucumber
2 green apples
2 celery stalks
1 thumb-size chunk
ginger
½ lemon

I guess that all juicers eventually develop their own basic combos for their favourite juices. This is my basic anytime juice, especially after a weekend of indulgent eating. It seems to settle and restore my system beautifully. You may end up developing your own favourites with time.

Benefits: This is a great cleansing juice for the liver, kidneys and digestive system. It also replaces the electrolytes that we lose through our daily activities. Electrolytes are important for the regulation of nerve and muscle function and for the body's hydration levels. These ingredients help reduce the acidity in the body, while their high dietary fibre and fluid content help to rid the body of toxins. These ingredients also help to make you feel full for longer and thereby help you to curb your appetite during your weight-loss programme. Ginger boosts the immune system, one of the reasons why it is such an essential part of Asian and Indian cuisine.

Handy hints: Both ginger and lemon contain properties that promote fat and waste elimination from the body, thereby complementing your weight-loss programme.

'Simple foods connect with your body's needs in complex ways.'
Bryant McGill

Juicing for health

It goes without saying that one of the primary objectives of juicing is to promote good health – for our loved ones and ourselves. Good health will always be balanced health, which is one of the things that intelligent juicing can help us achieve.

By knowing the nutritional benefits of the ingredients that are available to us, and by varying them from day to day, it will become possible for us to achieve that balance. For more information on how to acquire this knowledge it is worth consulting either of the helpful websites below (along with those that might be available in your region of the world or in your language of choice).

Another way juicing can be helpful in promoting health is when we use it to assist those with particular needs. For example, children who are resistant to eating fruit and vegetables are often more receptive to a well-blended juice containing those ingredients; and those recuperating from certain illnesses or surgical procedures that make eating or digesting difficult may also benefit in this way – if approved by their doctor.

Juicing can also be helpful on a seasonal basis prior to the proliferation of the annual cold and flu viruses, especially for children and the elderly, whose resistance should be maintained.

Hopefully you will find the following recipes helpful as you try to juice for health.

http://www.foodcounts.com/recommended-daily-allowances http://www.nutrition.org.uk

City haze

Every woman wants radiant, glowing skin. One of the effects of city life today is a suffering skin. Hydration and proper lubrication of the skin become crucial. This drink is particularly good for dry skin.

Benefits: If you have a dry skin problem it will not be remedied overnight, but will require an intentional inclusion in your diet of foods that lubricate and hydrate your skin. The skin is the largest organ of the body and can be beautifully maintained by including fresh fruit and vegetables in your daily diet. Foods that are specifically good for dry skin and which you should try to include in your daily menus include watermelon, papaya, mango, fennel, lime, parsley, watercress, avocado, Brazil nuts, coconut, celery, cucumber, garlic, ginger, basil, beetroot and all greens. Beautiful skin requires an adequate supply of vitamins A, E and K. Vitamin E gives your skin that beautiful 'dewy' look and is easily found in greens and nuts. Apparently a vitamin A deficiency contributes to acne. Foods rich in vitamin A include sweet potatoes, carrots, dark leafy greens, melons, bell peppers, fish, liver, and tropical fruits. Low levels of vitamin K are linked to easy bruising.

Handy hints: Create a moisturising avocado mask. Pit the fruit, purée the pulp, and pat it on your face. The oil softens and moisturises the skin and the vitamin E adds a glow to your skin.

Ingredients
Makes 2 glasses

1 papaya
1 cucumber
2 large ribs of celery
2 red apples
1 cup of greens (your choice)
Chunk of ginger

'We are not creators; only combiners of the created. Invention isn't about new ingredients, but new recipes. And innovations taste the best.'
Ryan Lilly

Beyond fifty

Ingredients
Makes 1 glass

1 grapefruit, peeled
1 cup mulberries/
strawberries
4 carrots

I want to be able to get up in the morning and not depend on my makeup kit to colour me beautiful. I want to be able to look at myself in the morning and like the face that I see in the mirror. I truly believe that having at least one juice a day can help me achieve that. Juicing alone will not give you a beautiful or ageless skin, but it can nourish your skin from inside.

Benefits: Grapefruit, carrots and mulberries are all excellent sources of vitamin C, an antioxidant that is important for beautiful skin. Vitamin C is naturally found in the skin and also helps the body to produce collagen, a protein that keeps your skin firm and elastic. This juice helps to replenish any lost vitamin C in the skin. Grapefruits are rich in potassium, which also helps to smooth wrinkles and age spots, and provides some protection against the harmful rays of the sun. Grapefruit refreshes the skin and the amino acids present in the grapefruit make the skin more firm and soft. Mulberries also contain a bit of vitamin A and vitamin E, which are both antioxidants and help nourish the skin. Mulberries are also an excellent source of the B-complex vitamins and vitamin K, which is said to protect the skin against bruising easily. Carrots are an excellent source of beta-carotene, an antioxidant that is converted to vitamin A inside the body. It helps to repair skin tissue and protect skin from sun damage.

Handy hints: Grapefruit can cause a negative reaction against many prescription drugs.

'Good nutrition is a result of a lifetime of daily good eating habits.'
Dr David Ailman, former president, AMA

Silica queen

Cucumber, celery and lemon are part of the basic juicing combination. They produce a slightly salty, slightly lemony tasting juice. But the addition of one radish will add a subtle sharp taste to the juice, which is not bad at all.

Ingredients
Makes 1 glass

1 cucumber
4 large celery stalks
1 radish
½ lemon

Benefits: These vegetables are all great sources of the vitamins and antioxidants necessary for beautiful skin. In addition to these antioxidants, both cucumbers and radishes are rich in silica. Silica gave our skin that youthful elasticity when we were young, but as we age we gradually lose this, and the skin begins to sag. Silica makes our bones stronger, our skin smoother, our hair shinier and our nails more beautiful. Brittle nails, weak hair and poor skin can all be signs of a silica deficiency. Gravity inevitably begins to pull our skin down and often wins, so using silica-rich foods makes good sense. In addition to radish and cucumber, try alfalfa, tomatoes, capsicum, wheatgrass, romaine lettuce and marjoram.

Handy hints: If you are looking for a way to interest your children in a vegetable garden, try radish. Radish grows rapidly and is the ideal first plant for a child's garden.

'Food is fuel: eat to live (don't live to eat)!'
Unknown

Leap for youth

Ingredients
Makes 1 glass

1 cucumber
½ beetroot
5 carrots
1 sprig marjoram

This is a very well-flavoured juice that you will like. It is a robust juice which is immensely satisfying and soothing to the system, and the strong pigmentation of the beetroot colours the juice red. If you don't have fresh marjoram you can add a pinch of dry herbs after juicing the other ingredients.

'Better a dry crust eaten in peace than a house filled with feasting – and conflict.'
Proverbs 17:1, NLT

Benefits: These vegetables provide a potent blend that will nourish and strengthen your skin, nails and hair. This juice will also strengthen the immune system, cleanse the body and improve your blood. It is actually also an excellent energy drink. Beetroot produces quite a bit of juice and you need very little of it to experience its benefits. Beetroot juice is also known to help to eliminate skin blemishes and skin inflammation.

Handy hints: Most beetroot we find on sale is round and red, but there are white, yellow and stripy types available too.

Juices for detoxing

One of the real benefits of juicing is the fact that – for most of us – it increases the amount of fluid that passes though our bodies. According to the Mayo Clinic, 'Nearly all of the major systems in your body depend on water.'[1] Among its benefits, the clinic points to three functions of water that have a direct bearing on the elimination and transportation of waste material from the body: it helps prevent constipation; it (through the blood) carries nutrients and oxygen to the cells, while also helping to remove waste products from them; and it lessens the burden on the liver and kidneys by helping to flush these waste products efficiently through those organs.

Another distinct benefit of juicing is that it helps to reduce the amount of animal-based food that our systems have to process. The widely accepted advantage of this is that one's cancer risk is reduced. As the Physicians Committee for Responsible Medicine[2] puts it, 'Vegetables and fruits help to reduce risk, while meat, animal products, and other fatty foods are frequently found to increase risk.' It goes on to make the point that: 'Meat is devoid of the protective effects of fibre, antioxidants, phytochemicals, and other helpful nutrients, and it contains high concentrations of saturated fat and potentially carcinogenic compounds, which may increase one's risk of developing many different kinds of cancer.'

Those are two good reasons to use the following fresh and tasty juicing recipes as part of your personal detox programme.

[1]http://www.mayoclinic.org/healthy-lifestyle/nutrition-and-healthy-eating/multimedia/functions-of-water-in-the-body/img-20005799 [2]http://www.pcrm.org/health/cancer-resources/diet-cancer/facts/meat-consumption-and-cancer-risk

Winter quickie

This juice has strong citrusy overtones but combines surprisingly well with the saltiness of celery and the taste of mint. I find this a quick feel-good juice when citrus fruits are in abundance.

Ingredients
Makes 1 glass

1 peeled grapefruit
1 peeled orange
3 stalks celery
Couple of mint leaves

Benefits: We would usually associate grapefruit with weight loss but it is also a winner when it comes to detoxing your body. Grapefruit, oranges and celery are known as excellent sources of vitamins, minerals and nutrients, and when you fill your body with good things it helps to get rid of some of the destructive toxins. Grapefruit not only helps the liver to burn up fat, but, like beetroot, it helps to flush the liver. Oranges and grapefruits are high in vitamin C but are also low in calories, and are good fruits for weight loss. Celery's alkalinity helps soothe the digestive system and mint is a herb that is rich in antioxidants and contains a small amount of vitamins and minerals.

Handy hints: The regular use of herbs, like mint, when cooking can help to cut down on our salt intake. Its nutritional value is also often overlooked.

Eat less sugar (you're sweet enough already).

Minty green

Ingredients
Makes 1 glass

2 cups spinach
4 kale leaves
2 sweet potatoes
¼ cup mint leaves
2 Granny Smith apples

There is a list of fruits, vegetables, seeds and herbs that are grouped together and seen as 'superfoods' because of their superior nutritional value. Spinach, kale, sweet potato and apples fit into that group. This juice is heavy, sweet and minty in flavour.

Benefits: Spinach and kale are green leafy vegetables that are rich in vitamins and nutrients. Besides containing high levels of vitamin K, both are good sources of calcium and manganese, which help to maintain bone density.

Sweet potatoes are a great source of antioxidants that help to protect the body against various diseases. Apple and sweet potato combine well in a juice. Juice the apples with their skin on because it is loaded with antioxidants.

Handy hints: Sweet potatoes are fat-free and cholesterol-free. They also have a lower glycaemic index than the white potato, keeping you fuller for longer.

Eating food is nourishment to the body. Preparing it is nourishment to the soul.

Energy snack

A sweet, zesty juice.

Benefits: Pear has a very high fibre content, which means that it is filling and an excellent food for the very young and the very old. It also helps with mild constipation. Apples are low in acid so they help to maintain a low acidic environment in the body. They are also the fruit with the richest vitamin E content and, as such, are very good for the skin. Pure apple juice seems to protect the body against kidney stones. Ginger also aids digestion. Parsley is a little herb that is rich in chlorophyll, vitamins, folate and iron, carotenoids and phytonutrients. You only need to add a small handful to your juice to benefit from its health properties. The pectin in the apple is also a great aid in detoxifying the body.

Handy hints: The apple 'diet' is well-known as a diet but it is perhaps less well-known as a 'fast' that cleanses your body of the accumulated wastes of wrong or excessive eating and drinking. Try and do it over a weekend, at least a couple of times a year, to detoxify your body.

Ingredients
Makes 1 glass

2 pears
1 green apple
4 carrots
2cm chunk ginger
Small handful parsley

'Women belong in the kitchen. Men belong in the kitchen. Everyone belongs in the kitchen. Kitchen has food.'
Unknown

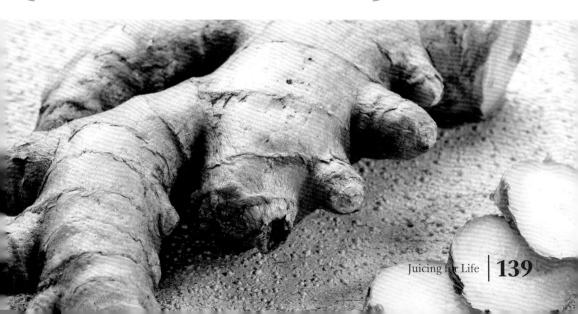

Greentox

Ingredients
Makes 2 glasses

4 Swiss chard leaves
2 cauliflower leaves
6 parsley sprigs
2 Pink Lady apples
½ lemon
1 cucumber
2 celery stalks
1cm chunk ginger

'A mother's diet in the first few days after conception could determine the health of her unborn child for life.'
Claire Ainsworth

All the cells, tissues and organs of the body require water to function optimally. Our body is constantly losing water throughout the day and a juice is a great way to replace lost body fluids and to energise the body.

Benefits: All edible green leaves are packed with life-giving and cleansing nutrients, minerals and B-complex vitamins. Vitamin B is important in maintaining cell health and converting food into energy, and healthy for the brain. Cucumber and celery help to flush toxins out of the body while also helping to hydrate the body and aid digestion. All such hydrating vegetables and fruits are good for detoxing the body's systems and organs.

Handy hints: Celery is one of the lowest-calorie foods that you can eat. It is virtually fat-free, making it an ideal snack for those of us who are seriously watching our weight.

Melon cleanser

Melon and carrot make a gloriously orange juice that is also a wonderful cleanser.

Benefits: The bright orange colour of the crunchy carrot is an indication that it is packed with antioxidants. Carrot is an excellent source of vitamin A and vitamin K. It is one of the vegetables that contain carotenoids, which offer protection against heart disease, help to prevent macular degeneration and help to regulate blood sugar. Carrots are also low in calories, making them a great vegetable for weight loss. The sweet melon is a wonderful cleansing fruit, especially of the kidneys, and helps to alkalise the body. If you have access to organic melon, juice the rind too because it contains many health-giving minerals and enzymes. Ginger is a root that has many beneficial properties, especially a group of antioxidants known as gingerols, which protect the body against inflammation, viruses and various diseases.

Handy hints: Onions and garlic are usually seen as powerful anticoagulants. But ginger is actually better at preventing the formation of blood clots in the body than they are.

Ingredients
Makes 2 glasses

½ sweet melon/
cantaloupe
5 carrots
2cm chunk ginger

'In France, cooking is a serious art form and a national sport.'
Julia Child

Cleanup

Beetroot colours every juice red, but it also adds a pleasant sweetness to the mix.

Ingredients
Makes 2 glasses

1 beetroot
1-2 apples
1 cucumber
3 Swiss chard leaves
½ lemon

'Good health is not something we can buy. However, it can be an extremely valuable savings account.'
Anne Wilson Schaef

Benefits: Beetroots are amazingly juicy and filling, and, together with the apples, cucumber and lemon, they hydrate the body and replenish vitamins, minerals and nutrients. Apples contain pectin, a fibre that helps to flush toxins out of the digestive tract, making the work of the liver easier. Apples are also high in soluble fibre, which aids the digestive process.

Handy hints: Drinking warm water with freshly squeezed lemon in the morning helps to stimulate the liver.

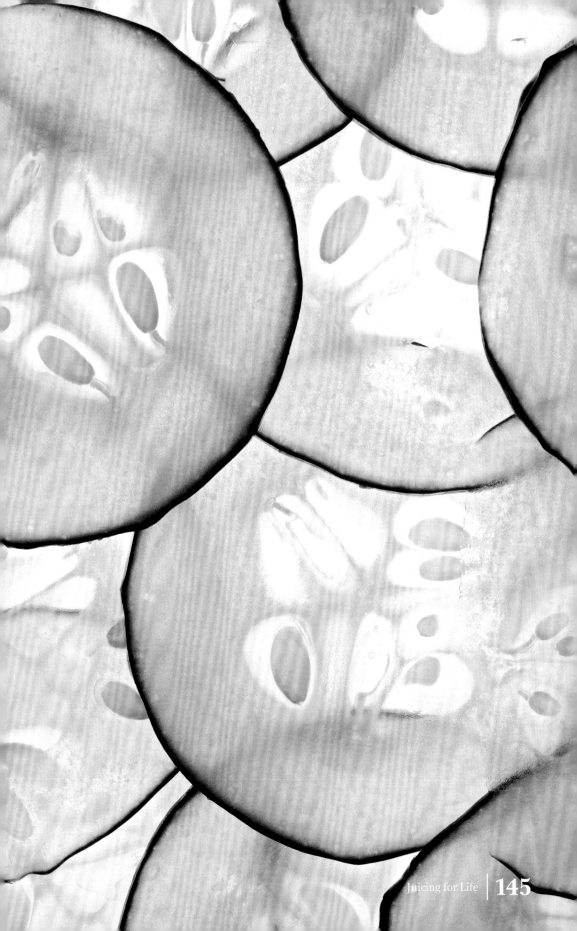

Smoothies

Breakfast smoothies

I firmly believe that we cannot live on juices or smoothies alone. Neither will a smoothie 'smooth out' my bad eating habits and miraculously cure me of every illness that I have.

On the other hand, they do allow me to blend together a combination of fruits, vegetables, herbs and nuts that can nourish my body with nutrients, minerals, vitamins, antioxidants and energy. I am also able to vary the combinations according to my needs and tastes, and to replace a meal with a smoothie without any damage to my body.

Smoothies blend whole foods together and are often more substantial than a juice because they include all that fabulous fibre for sustained fullness.

Smoothies can be made to appeal to all taste buds – give them a try.

Mango filler

A quick, light breakfast on a summer morning. I love the combination of mango and peach. The peach should be very ripe, oozing juice. The smell is irresistible. Especially good on a morning after you've had a filling supper the night before. The yoghurt adds some protein that fills you up.

Benefits: Mango helps to alkalise the whole body because it contains tartaric, malic and citric acid. Fresh mango freezes well, for that out-of-season smoothie. Mangoes are rich in vitamins B6, C and E, which aid the body in fighting infection. Peaches are a good source of vitamins A, C, and fibre. Not only is vitamin A essential for night vision, but it also assists in maintaining healthy mucous membranes and the quality of our skin.

Handy hints: Mango pulp and mango juice reduce body heat. So when your energy is depleted after a day in the sun and your body feels all hot and bothered, have a mango.

Ingredients
Makes 2 glasses

1 mango
1 peach
½ cup plain yoghurt
4 ice blocks
A handful of frozen blackberries

Nothing brings people together like good food.

Pear refresher

A light, mild-tasting blend of fruits and seeds, flavoured with cinnamon and vanilla. The dates sweeten the smoothie. For a more substantial smoothie you could add half a cup of rolled oats or half a cup of soaked barley.

Ingredients

Makes 3 glasses

3 pears
1 peach
4 dates, soaked
2 tbsp mixed seeds
½ cup plain yoghurt
¼ tsp cinnamon
½ tsp vanilla extract
½ cup milk

'Good nutrition is not a proverbial fountain of youth, but it can help. . . .'
Dr David Ailman, former president, AMA

Benefits: Yoghurt and milk provide B12, which maintains red blood cells and helps keep your nervous system functioning properly. They are also good sources of potassium, phosphorus, riboflavin, iodine, zinc, and other B vitamins. The high content of pectin in pears is helpful in lowering cholesterol levels but it also functions as a diuretic and has a mild laxative effect. Drinking pear juice regularly helps regulate bowel movements and pear fibre is highly beneficial for your colon health.

Handy hints: An interesting difference in the way that cinnamon is used is that in the West, cinnamon is used for preparing sweet things like desserts and pies, but in India, it is used more often for savoury things like curries.

Berry breakfast

This is a good smoothie for those who need a substantial breakfast. Put the liquids into the blender first and then add the solids. The combination of oats, fruit and yoghurt is a common one, and one can experiment with any number of variations. When I wake up with a growling stomach, I like to add a little oatmeal to my morning smoothie.

Benefits: Rolled oats are traditionally oat groats that have been de-husked and rolled out. Oats are a good source of protein, carbohydrates and fat but if you have too much raw oatmeal the calorie count climbs. It is possible to use soy, almond or rice milk.

Berries are packed with all kinds of nutrients and healthy antioxidants, and cranberries rank at the top. It is a good idea to add some, fresh or frozen, to a smoothie. If you don't have access to fresh dates, soak the dry ones in some hot water for 5 minutes before blending. This smoothie is definitely for those who are not counting calories.

Handy hints: For thousands of years in Africa, Asia and along the Mediterranean, people have been eating raw fruit for dessert.

Ingredients
Makes 3 glasses

1 cup milk
½ cup rolled oats
½ cup strawberry yoghurt
2 cored and chopped pears
10 frozen cranberries
6 dates
½ tsp vanilla extract
¼ tsp ground cinnamon

'Only a fool argues with a skunk, a mule or a cook.'
Cowboy saying

Persimmon choc

Ingredients
Makes 2 glasses

2 persimmons
2 apples
½ cup Greek yoghurt
¼ cup rolled oats
1 tsp cocoa
1 tsp honey
¼ cup milk
1 banana

For those who crave a little sweetness in the morning, this smoothie hits the spot. The honey, persimmon and banana add the sweetness, while the cocoa and banana will enhance your mood.

Benefits: Bananas are rich in magnesium, which helps to relieve cramps. They are also very low in saturated fat, cholesterol and sodium, as well as being a good source of dietary fibre. Being rich in potassium, the banana is an excellent food for the maintenance of brain and heart efficiency. A completely ripe persimmon fruit is soft, very sweet and tasty, and has a good combination of nutrients in moderate quantities. Persimmons are high in fibre, making you feel fuller for longer. Cocoa helps to stimulate the 'feel-good' chemicals in the brain known as serotonin and dopamine.

Handy hints: Rub a bug bite with the inside of a banana leaf to relieve the itching.

Annoying the cook will result in smaller portions.

Breakfast bang

This is quite a filling smoothie due to the combination of dairy, banana and oats. The cranberries give it a reddish tinge that seems to make it more enjoyable to drink. I liked the way that the subtle tastes of the banana and pear were complemented by the tart sweetness of the pineapple and cranberries. A very fruity smoothie enhanced by the immunity-boosting power of lemon.

Ingredients
Makes 3 glasses

1 cup milk
½ cup plain yoghurt
1 banana
2 pears
10 cranberries
½ small pineapple
½ tsp cinnamon
½ tsp vanilla extract
½ cup rolled oats
½ small lemon (include skin if organic)

Benefits: There are high levels of tryptophan in the banana, which the body converts into serotonin, a feel-good, mood-elevating chemical. Like banana, pineapple is high in potassium and low in sodium, which helps maintain normal blood pressure. Pineapples are a great source of bromelain, which is thought to help prevent sinusitis and have the capability to fight off inflammation that may affect the tissues and organs in the body. Pineapple is also a great detoxing agent and is known to help relieve morning sickness and nausea.

Handy hints: 'Dutch researchers recently reported that higher dairy consumption (mainly from milk and yoghurt) was modestly linked to lower blood pressure in 2,064 Dutch men and women ages 50 to 75' (*www.webmd.com/food-recipes/benefits-yogurt*).

'Food should be fun.'
Thomas Keller

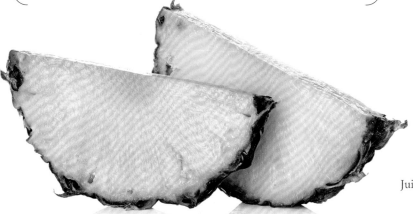

Pineapple and spinach

Ingredients
Makes 2 glasses

4 spinach leaves
¼ chopped pineapple
4 tbsp plain yoghurt
½ cup water
1 banana

On paper it looks like an odd combination – spinach, pineapple and banana – but it actually works. Pineapple is especially good to have if you've pigged out at the dessert table the night before and you need some cleansing. The banana and yoghurt settle the stomach, give the smoothie a creamy texture and, more importantly, fill you up.

Benefits: Spinach is virtually fat, sugar and cholesterol-free. Each cup of raw spinach contains only 7 calories, so it is a wise addition to your diet if you are trying to lose weight. Spinach is a good source of vitamin A, which keeps your skin, bones and teeth healthy. Pineapples are a rich source of antioxidants, which help the body resist diseases. Pineapple is also known for its anti-inflammatory properties.

Handy hints: Pineapples don't have any starch reserves that can turn to sugar, so the only thing that happens when you let it sit out is that it over-ripens and starts to ferment.

'First we eat, then we do everything else.'
M. F. K. Fisher

Mango smoothie

Mango is known by some as 'the king of fruit' and, together with apricots, is the taste of southern hemisphere summer for me. The blend of the two fruits is both sweet and tangy at the same time, with the nutmeg adding a spicy twist to the mixture. This smoothie could easily double up as a light dessert to finish off a heavy meal.

Ingredients
Makes 2 glasses

1 ripe mango, peeled, pitted and chopped
4 apricots
½ cup plain yoghurt
4 dates/2 tbsp puréed dates
¼ cup milk
Pinch of nutmeg

Benefits: Mango is diabetic-friendly because it has a low glycaemic index, resulting in a slow release of sugar into the body; therefore it should not drastically affect your sugar levels. Anaemia sufferers and menopausal and pregnant women can enjoy mangoes as this will increase their iron levels and, for the women, calcium at the same time. Dates are good for gaining weight, for those rare individuals who need help. They are also a good source of energy, sugar and fibre, making them an excellent pre-workout food. Dates that are soaked overnight and eaten will greatly assist individuals suffering from constipation.

Handy hints: Mango is regarded to have aphrodisiac qualities and apparently increases virility in men. It is rich in vitamin E, which is thought to regulate sex hormones and boost sex drive.

'Gluttony is an emotional escape, a sign something is eating us.'
Peter De Vries

Evening snack

Ingredients
Makes 2 glasses

2 ripe pears
1 banana
8 almonds
½ cup strawberry
yoghurt
4 dates (soak in hot
water while you load
the blender and add
last)
1 cup milk

'Laughter is
brightest, where
food is best.'
Irish proverb

Blend well and sweet dreams! Almonds are good brain food and the banana will help you have a good sleep. It's a sweeter than usual smoothie, so watch out for too much of it.

Benefits: There are approximately 578 calories in 100 grams of almonds. According to some calorie counters, the calorie breakdown for 100 grams of almonds is about: 73% fat, 14% carbs, 13% protein. There is no sodium, potassium or cholesterol in this nut. You can go nuts with almonds if you are not calorie watching. If you are lactose intolerant you could use almond milk instead of dairy. Will eating a banana before bedtime actually help you sleep? Bananas are rich in potassium and magnesium, which are muscle relaxants, and in this way they help your body prepare for sleep.

Handy hints: Almonds cannot self-pollinate and need bees to help them do so. Without bees, you would have no almonds at all! Save the bees!

Orange glow

A simple, creamy and filling smoothie, to which nutmeg gives a slight spiciness. You can use butternut or any kind of pumpkin.

Benefits: Pumpkin and pumpkin seeds are very good for you. The seeds are high in fibre, keeping you fuller for longer. Pumpkin seeds are rich in tryptophan, which helps the body make serotonin, the feel-good neurotransmitter that helps you relax and improves your mood. Pumpkin comes in as a weight-loss winner with only about 50 calories per cup. It is also good for eyesight because it is so rich in vitamin A. It also helps to keep your skin, eyes and mucous membranes moist and healthy. Unlike dairy milk, coconut milk is lactose-free and can be used as a milk substitute by those with lactose intolerance.

Handy hints: Potassium helps restore the body's balance of electrolytes after a heavy workout and keeps muscles in good form. Cooked pumpkin is high in potassium.

Ingredients
Makes 2 glasses

2 cups cooked pumpkin
1 cup coconut milk
¼ tsp nutmeg

'Good nutrition does not come overnight. And it is not a hit-or-miss proposition.'
Dr David Ailman, former president, AMA

Minty nut

Ingredients
Makes 3 glasses

1 papaya
2 persimmons
2 spinach leaves
1 sprig garden mint
Small chunk ginger
Handful mixed
cashews and almonds
¼ cup plain yoghurt
2 tsp honey

If you want
breakfast in bed,
sleep in the
kitchen.

A light but filling green smoothie packed with vitamins and nutrients that keeps you going for hours. You can serve this chilled or with ice cubes, but I prefer it straight from the blender for breakfast. It has a lovely mint taste.

Benefits: Persimmon, also known as the 'food from the gods', provides about 55% of the body's daily requirement of vitamin A and 21% of its requirement of vitamin C. It is an excellent source of fibre and B-complex vitamins, which help your body to convert protein, carbohydrates and fat into energy. Fresh papaya is also a rich source of the minerals magnesium, potassium, phosphorus and iron.

Handy hints: Persimmon is a fruit with a very high fructose content so it should be consumed in moderation.

Green smoothies

The green smoothie provides an opportunity for us to help our children (and the odd reluctant or recuperating adult) to eat important vegetables that they may otherwise choose to ignore. Smoothies also help to keep the body hydrated, something which is useful during the warmer months.

Green vegetables provide a good source of minerals and vitamins and, according to a spokesperson for the Academy of Nutrition and Dietetics, 'Vegetables are high in potassium, which can help lower blood pressure. If the vegetables are puréed so that the fibre is still intact, they will [also] help fill you up.'*

There is something else to bear in mind, however, for if the intended users are either diabetics or suffering with kidney stones they should be careful about what they blend into their smoothies. Those who are susceptible to calcium oxalate kidney stones should be aware that raw spinach and Swiss chard contain higher levels of oxalates. Those with diabetes will want to watch the amount of carbohydrates in their smoothies, which could affect their blood sugar levels; and creams or other high-fat additions can add fat and calories to smoothies.

These cautions aside, spinach is a great green veg to use in smoothies, as are celery, kale, beetroot leaves, cucumber and parsley: all of which partner well with green apples and kiwi fruit. What follows are some recipes that I have found tasty and nutritious, but I am sure that you will soon discover your own!

*http://www.usatoday.com/story/news/nation/2013/08/03/green-smoothies-nutrition/2518141/

So smooth

At first I didn't really enjoy the taste of this smoothie, because it was too fresh-tasting. But after adding two pinches of my favourite cayenne pepper and a pinch of salt, that did it for me.

Benefits: Spinach is a really amazing food that is low in saturated fat and cholesterol and a good source of essential vitamins and minerals. Spinach is high in plant-based sodium, which is vital to our cell health and development.

Handy hints: Vitamin K is a fat-soluble vitamin that is most well-known for the important role it plays in blood clotting. This vitamin received its designation from the first letter of the German term for 'coagulation vitamin', namely, *koagulationsvitamin*.

Ingredients
Makes 2 glasses

2 cups baby spinach
2 pears, unpeeled
1 banana
1 small, ripe avocado
Handful frozen cranberries
Pinch of salt and cayenne

'Gardening is a form of physical activity that allows you to be productive while enjoying the great outdoors.'
Andrew Cate

Blackie

Ingredients
Makes 2 glasses

2-3 cups organic spinach
1 cup milk or juice
1 banana
½ cup frozen blackberries
3 ice cubes

This is a green smoothie but the blackberries change the colour somewhat. In spite of that it still contains a healthy dose of spinach that is packed with nutrients and vitamins. Although it is not a heavy smoothie, it is still quite substantial because of the banana and milk. For a more substantial smoothie add a quarter-cup of oats.

Benefits: Blackberries contain an impressive range of minerals, including calcium, iron, magnesium, phosphorus, potassium and zinc. They are also an excellent source of amino acids and essential dietary fibre. The health benefits of berries are generally well-known, but blackberry benefits include better digestive health, a strengthened immune system, better heart health, and help in the prevention of cancer.

Handy hints: The dark-blue colour of the blackberry indicates that it has exceptionally high antioxidant levels.

Food is our common ground, a universal experience!

Autumn smoothie

Pumpkin is an all-time autumn favourite that has almost no fat, but adds a creamy thick consistency to any smoothie. It's also loaded with antioxidants, like alpha and beta-carotene, which are converted into vitamin A in the body. The combined flavour of pumpkin and coconut is quite yummy. Cinnamon adds a very slight spiciness.

Benefits: Coconut milk is high in calories. One cup gives you over 500 calories. Coconut milk is one of the few foods that are rich in lauric acid, which helps the body fight germs, viruses and fungi, and it is also rich in vitamins B, C and E. Vitamins C and E help to boost the immune system, and the B-complex vitamins are responsible for providing energy to the cells. I've added a quarter-cup of cashews for flavour, but they are also nutrient-dense as well as being rich in good (unsaturated) fatty acids.

Handy hints: Once you've opened a can of coconut milk, refrigerate the contents because its high oil content will make it turn rancid very quickly.

Ingredients
Makes 2 glasses

3 kale leaves
½ cup coconut milk
1 banana, frozen
¼ teaspoon cinnamon
½ cup pumpkin purée
¼ teaspoon vanilla extract
¼ cup cashew nuts

Cooking with love provides food for the soul.

Midday energiser

A very fresh-tasting smoothie, and not for the faint-hearted. Wow! But a great afternoon energy drink.

Ingredients
Makes 3 glasses

2 cups chopped fresh kale
2 avocados
10 garden mint leaves
½ lemon
2 cups water
Add a pinch of salt and cayenne pepper to each glass
Serve over ice

Benefits: Fresh kale makes a super base for a green smoothie. Not only does the chlorophyll give a dense colour to the smoothie, but it also has healing benefits such as the relief of constipation, detoxification and wound healing. Beta-carotene and vitamin C work to protect your intestine and colon. Avocado is a high-fat food containing a monounsaturated fatty substance called oleic acid. This thick yellow oil is good for retaining moisture in skin and hair. Cayenne pepper has been used as a natural supportive treatment for a variety of ailments including heartburn, gout, paralysis, fever, dyspepsia, flatulence, sore throat, nausea and tonsillitis. I sometimes add more than a pinch of cayenne to my smoothies.

Handy hints: Mix mashed avocado with lemon juice for a basic avocado facial mask. Avocado deep-cleanses, moisturises and nourishes the skin.

'We are too accustomed to going to stores and purchasing what we need.'
Ezra Taft Benson

Nutty greens

❤ 🏃

It was 'Popeye the sailor man' who popularised spinach as a super strength-building food. While its strength-building qualities may be debatable, we all know that spinach is good for us. The yoghurt, peanut butter and spinach combination provides a good supply of omega-3s, which are good for the heart because they may help lower blood pressure and reduce blood clotting.

Benefits: Spinach is nutrient-rich but wonderfully low in calories. One of its important nutrients is dietary magnesium, which our bodies use to help maintain our muscles and nerves, our heart rhythm, a healthy immune system and optimum blood pressure. Spinach is also a great source of iron. If there is too little iron in the blood it means that the blood cannot carry enough oxygen to the cells, and this can adversely affect our energy levels.

Handy hints: Slice the banana into usable portions before freezing. This makes for easier blending.

Ingredients
Makes 2 glasses

½ cup plain yoghurt
1 cup coconut milk
1 tablespoon natural peanut butter
2 cups spinach
1 frozen banana
½ cup fresh strawberries
¼ cup roasted almonds

'A healthy attitude is contagious but don't wait to catch it from others. Be a carrier.'
Tom Stoppard

Soothing green

Ingredients
Makes 1 glass

2 spinach leaves
1 pear
½ cucumber
¼ small lemon
1 celery stalk + leaves
½ cup water

'Seeds and nuts
are indispensable
for cardiovascular
health.'
Joel Fuhrman

This makes a hydrating, filling smoothie with a slightly lemony taste. Spinach always makes a good base for a green smoothie or juice.

Benefits: By now you are aware of the many nutritional benefits of spinach, pears and cucumbers. The combination of these three ingredients with celery and lemon juice also ensures that this smoothie will be a low-calorie, low-fat drink, ideal for when we want to maintain or reduce our weight.

Handy hints: If you are on medication you need to check (with your dietician or doctor) to ensure that you are not taking in more of a certain vitamin or mineral than your body needs.

Citrusy green

Papaya is one of my favourite fruits. It is a sweet and soft tropical fruit that requires very little chewing. The inside flesh is a rich orange in colour but mild in taste. When combined with citrus, ginger and coriander, however, papaya adds the substance to make this smoothie a winner.

Benefits: Papayas are a natural source of vitamins A and C and lots of beta-carotene. Beta-carotene is the yellow/orange pigment that gives vegetables and fruits their vivid colours, and which the body converts into vitamin A. Having a daily intake of such fruits could help reduce inflammation in those who suffer with diseases that affect the joints. Papaya is an easy fruit for young and old to eat.

Clementines are usually juicy and sweet, with less acid than oranges. This fruit can be substituted by the tangerine, or the *naartjie* as they commonly call them in South Africa.

Handy hints: Transform a normal green salad into something special by adding papaya, ginger, coriander and lemon zest.

Ingredients
Makes 2 small glasses

1 small papaya
2 clementines, peeled
3 spinach leaves
Small handful almonds
1cm fresh ginger
Small handful coriander

'If most of us valued food and cheer and song above hoarded gold, it would be a merrier world.'
J. R. R. Tolkien

A green surprise

Ingredients
Makes 2 glasses

1 cup baby spinach
1 cup papaya
1 peeled orange
1 medium sweet
potato (microwaved,
boiled or baked till
soft)
¼ cup cashew nuts

Spinach is the base for this smoothie, but when I am really hungry I like to add a cooked sweet potato instead of yoghurt. It makes me feel fuller somehow. Blending cooked sweet potato and cashew nuts delivers a very creamy smoothie. Pop a sweet potato into the microwave and try this one for breakfast or supper. Sweet potato also combines well with orange and other citrus fruits.

Benefits: Sweet potatoes are a good source of beta-carotene and vitamins B5 and B6, as well as copper and other life-sustaining minerals. They have a medium glycaemic index, so this option might be better than ordinary potatoes for those who have to watch their blood sugar levels. Although they contain more sugar than regular potatoes, sweet potatoes are fat-free and have fewer calories than regular potatoes. The baby spinach does not have as strong a taste as grown spinach leaves, so it blends in well with the cooked sweet potato and the juicy papaya.

Handy hints: Both sweet potato and papaya contain very little sodium, which makes them good foods to keep your skin hydrated.

'My cooking is so awesome, even the smoke alarm cheers me on!'
Quotes Love and Life.com

Garden fresh

This smoothie resulted from a random selection of leaves chosen when I went into my veggie garden before breakfast one day, and it worked! Harvest your leaves before the sun begins to burn them and they wilt. The tartness of the Granny Smith apple and the ginger combined well with the leaves. Why not add some oats if you are facing a day of strenuous physical activity?

Benefits: This smoothie will give you a tasty drink, rich with the nutrients and minerals that are found in the combined green leaves. You will have energy from the protein in the yoghurt and that should keep you filled up for a bit. This amount of coconut milk has about 2.3g of protein, which should add to your feeling of satiety and ensure a slow release of energy. If you love the taste of coconut milk you could increase the amount to half a cup because it is a good source of iron, magnesium and vitamin C. Besides adding a spicy zest to this smoothie, ginger helps settle the stomach for the day.

Handy hints: Plain yoghurt is very versatile. Flavour it yourself with various fruits and honey. You can also use it as a topping for potatoes or pies, or as a healthier substitute for mayonnaise.

Ingredients
Makes 1 glass

1 bowl mixed baby leaves (kale, spinach, beetroot, cauliflower, mint, rocket and lettuce)
½ cup plain yoghurt
1 small green apple, peeled
Small chunk ginger
¼ cup coconut milk

'I don't need a fancy party to be happy. Just good friends, good food, and good laughs.'
Maria Sharapova

Green anytime

Ingredients
Makes 3 glasses

1 large mango
1 400ml tin coconut
milk
2 cups baby spinach or
baby kale
1 banana
½ tsp cinnamon

This is a delicious anytime smoothie. Coconut blends particularly well with mango and banana. You can almost not taste the spinach or kale in this smoothie, while the spiciness of cinnamon completes the taste.

Benefits: We have already mentioned how good mangoes are for our health in general. In particular, mango is good for anaemia sufferers, and menopausal and pregnant women, because it increases their iron and calcium levels. Spinach is virtually fat, sugar and cholesterol-free. Each cup of raw spinach contains only 7 calories, so it tempers the richness of this smoothie.

Handy hints: Cinnamon is a very versatile spice that is used in both sweet and savoury dishes. It is commonly used in curries, or sprinkled over puddings or pancakes along with some sugar.

'I don't think there are bad cooks, just bad recipes.'
Deb Perelman

Workout smoothies

Before we get down to making the workout smoothies work for us, let's take a moment to reflect on some sound advice about nutrition and exercise.*

1. Plan and prepare your smoothies in relation to the amount of exercise you intend to do. Bear in mind that high-intensity training will require more calories than a gentle walk, and don't confuse the smoothie requirements!

2. Get to know how your body regulates blood sugar, and if in doubt chat to a nutritionist or your doctor. Essentially you need to know how long you can last during a workout before 'hitting the wall' – that point at which your stores of glycogen in the liver and muscles are depleted.

3. Be clear about your fitness goals. For example, do you want to build muscle or lose weight? As Johns Hopkins nutritionist Joshua Nachman has said, 'A 500-calorie smoothie after an hour of weight training is fine if you're trying to build muscle, but not if you're trying to lose weight.'

Now you can get to work on those workout smoothies!

Source: http://www.hopkinsmedicine.org/health/healthy_heart/eat_smart/fuel-your-fitness

The energiser

This is another good pre-workout smoothie that will boost your energy levels for a strenuous session. Banana, papaya, raisins and honey are especially good energy foods.

Ingredients
Makes 2 glasses

1 banana
1 cup papaya
½ tsp cinnamon
1 tsp honey
½ cup plain yoghurt
¼ cup milk of choice
10 almonds
1 tbsp raisins

Benefits: Bananas boost our energy and contain a good amount of potassium. Potassium is a mineral that is easily lost during sweating but is essential for the body's cellular and electrical functioning. From this it is easy to see that a vegetable or fruit smoothie can really help to replace minerals and electrolytes that are lost during exercise. Ripe, juicy papaya is also a great natural energy food that is easily digested. Almonds reduce the glycaemic index of the juice, resulting in a slow release of sugar during a workout for sustained energy. The glycaemic index, or GI, measures how a carbohydrate-rich food affects the blood sugar. It is especially useful for diabetics to understand which foods will reduce or increase their GI. Including almonds in a meal can help keep your blood sugar under control.

Handy hints: Add a handful of lightly roasted almonds to your salad. You can pan-roast your own almonds by putting them into a dry, heated pan and stirring them around for a few minutes.

'When a man's stomach is full it makes no difference whether he is rich or poor.'
Euripides

Peachy cream

Ingredients
Makes 2 glasses

½ cup rolled oats
½ cup peach yoghurt
½ cup milk
½ medium banana
1 ripe peach
1 tbsp chia seeds
(soaked for a few
minutes)
¼ tsp cinnamon
½ tsp vanilla extract

'Then God said,
"Look! I have
given you every
seed-bearing plant
throughout the
earth and all the
fruit trees for
food." '
Genesis 1:29, NLT

Blend this smoothie only after the chia seeds have been soaked. The oats and banana make this quite a filling smoothie and the protein in the milk and yoghurt will help sustain you during your workout.

Benefits: Oats are a good source of protein and carbohydrates, and rolled oats have a low glycaemic index. The glycaemic index, or GI, measures how carbohydrates in food affect our blood sugar. Food with a high GI raises blood sugar more than food with a medium or low GI. But the amount of carbohydrates you consume is as important as the GI, because all the carbs add up. Foods with a low GI include legumes, all non-starchy vegetables, some starchy vegetables like sweet potatoes, most fruit, and many wholegrain breads and cereals, like rolled oats. Bananas are always a good addition because of their high potassium content.

Handy hints: Chia seeds have become a new weight-loss champion because they expand significantly in water and help you feel full for longer.

Watermelon fresher

Who can resist the smell of sliced fresh watermelon on a warm summer day? Watermelons come in all shapes and sizes depending on where you live, but they are all easily juiced to provide a treat that is both tasty and hydrating.

Benefits: Watermelon is mostly water, about 90%, but it is also full of electrolytes that help the body maintain normal fluid levels during your workout. Apparently watermelon juice can also help to reduce muscle soreness after a workout. You can replenish your energy levels before and after a workout by having a serving of yoghurt within an hour of the session. Greek yoghurt in particular provides you with a good source of protein and calcium, besides having the fewest carbs of the various types of yoghurt. Strawberries are full of nutrients and sugar for energy.

Handy hints: In Israel and Egypt, the sweet taste of watermelon is often paired with the salty taste of feta cheese. Why not pile these onto a bed of lettuce and rocket for a quick refreshing summer salad, to which you can add a bit of chilli, if that takes your fancy?

Ingredients
Makes 2 glasses

7 cups watermelon, cubed
½ cup strawberries
½ cup Greek yoghurt

'A crust eaten in peace is better than a banquet partaken in anxiety.'
Aesop

Banana energy

Ingredients
Makes 2 glasses

1 banana
⅓ cup rolled oats
1 cup milk
4 dates (soak in
hot water for a few
minutes)
½ tsp cocoa

Bananas often form the basis for energy smoothies because of their high potassium content and the energy that they provide during a workout. This smoothie is a thick one, packed with energy, and ready to kick-start your exercise session.

Benefits: As we already know, bananas are rich in magnesium, which helps to relieve muscle cramps during a workout, and potassium, which is a wonderful energy-supplying electrolyte. Oats are a good source of protein and carbohydrates, and release energy gradually to help sustain you during your session. Cocoa helps to stimulate the feel-good chemicals in the brain known as serotonin and dopamine. We all need to feel good while exercising, especially in that period before the endorphins kick in.

Handy hints: Enjoying a banana a bit before bedtime should help you to sleep better at night because of its vitamin B6.

'Too many
people just eat to
consume calories.
Try dining for a
change.'
John Walters

Fruity yoghurt

Banana and strawberries sliced into Greek yoghurt create a stunningly simple dessert, but they also work well together as a basis for this smoothie.

Benefits: Both bananas and strawberries are known as high-energy fruits, but not so well-known is the fact that berries are a good workout recovery food, rich in polyphenol antioxidants which are thought to help protect the cells from damage and pain. Oats and yoghurt are good sources of slow-release proteins and carbohydrates. Chia seeds originate in South America and derive their name from the ancient Mayan word for 'strength'. Since their discovery they are also being used as a strong energy food by those who are health conscious.

Handy hints: Soak the chia seeds before use. They absorb a tremendous amount of water, which will make you feel full for longer.

Ingredients
Makes 2 glasses

1 banana
1 cup strawberries
¼ cup rolled oats
½ cup Greek yoghurt
1 tbsp chia seeds

'If it scares you it might be a good thing to try.'
Seth Godin

Savoury surprise

Ingredients
Makes 2 glasses

1 small glass carrot juice
1 small avocado (like the Hass variety)
1 tbsp fresh lemon juice
1 tbsp coconut oil
1 tbsp freshly grated ginger
Pinch of cayenne pepper

A messy kitchen is a sign of happiness.

Although ginger adds spice, it also complements the humble carrot in this smoothie. The lemon juice and ginger give this drink quite a pungent flavour.

Benefits: A cup of carrot juice is rich with protein and natural sugar, making it a good vegetable choice for an energy smoothie. Avocado contains saturated fats, folic acid, vitamin K, vitamin C, vitamin E and pantothenic acid. It is a good source of potassium that boosts energy levels. Ginger seems to help with the easing of both menstrual pain and exercise-induced muscle pain. Cayenne pepper has also been shown to boost the metabolism. The coconut oil adds some good fat.

Handy hints: Steep peeled fresh ginger in boiling water for five minutes to make your own ginger tea. Add some honey and lemon if you'd like.

Nutty creamed melon

This is a simply super sweet smoothie to have after a workout to replenish the body. A melon is almost all water so it makes an excellent smoothie to hydrate your body too. The softness of the melon flavours complements the yoghurt beautifully.

Benefits: Sweet melon is a good source of vitamins and minerals like potassium, which increases energy during your workout. But having a melon smoothie also helps to hydrate the body after a workout and replenishes the cells. Melon is also a great kidney and bladder cleanser. The yoghurt and nuts also provide good protein for slow energy release as you work out.

Handy hints: Both melons and citrus fruits contain more potassium than bananas.

Ingredients
Makes 3 glasses

1 sweet melon, peeled and seeded
1 cup plain Greek yoghurt
1 small handful cashews

'The most important principle of eating well is selecting a variety of foods.'
Mark Finley and Peter Landless, Health & Wellness: Secrets that Will Change Your Life

Green vitality

Ingredients
Makes 2 glasses

2 cups fresh kale
(young leaves)
1 cup coconut milk
1 orange, peeled
1 cup chopped
pineapple
1 cup mixed berries
2 tbsp chopped garden
mint

I would not use mature kale leaves for a smoothie because they can have a rather bitter, strong taste. Steam the kale for about five minutes before blending.

Benefits: Kale has become known as a nutritional powerhouse. It is a dream vegetable for those wanting to lose weight, because it is low in calories, high in fibre and has zero fat. It is also high in vitamin C, which helps to maintain cartilage and joint flexibility and helps keep the body hydrated. Both pineapple and orange contain potassium, an important electrolyte that helps the body restore its fluid levels after a workout. Berries, as already mentioned, add wonderful restorative antioxidants to a smoothie, although they also change the colour of the smoothie.

Handy hints: It is fun to grow pineapples but it takes at least two years for a pineapple plant to bear fruit, even in the best conditions.

'As a child my family's menu consisted of two choices: take it or leave it.'
Buddy Hackett

Beetroot power

It is interesting to see a juice made with beetroot for the first time. It doesn't matter what else is in the mix: beetroot turns everything dark red. Although I love beetroot, I had to be persuaded to try the juice at first. Now I don't mind whether it is juiced raw or boiled; I love its sweetness.

Benefits: Beetroot juice is a great way to boost stamina and make muscles work harder during a training session. It contains potassium, magnesium and iron, plus carbohydrates, protein, powerful antioxidants and soluble fibre. Beetroot seems to be quite an underestimated vegetable. Carrots have a high natural sugar content but this natural sugar is easily assimilated. If you are diabetic you might want to watch your carrot intake though. The two biggest health benefits of lemons are a) their strong antibacterial, antiviral, and immune-boosting powers, and b) their use as a weight-loss aid, because lemon juice is a known digestive aid and liver cleanser.

Handy hints: Grate raw beetroot and add it to coleslaw or your favourite salad. You could also try topping roasted beetroot with goat's cheese for a delicious food combination.

Ingredients
Makes 2 glasses

3 medium beetroots, parboiled
2 large carrots
2 Granny Smith apples
1 3-inch piece fresh ginger, grated finely
1 tbsp fresh lemon juice

'Eat little, sleep sound.'
Iranian proverb

Nutty choc

Ingredients
Makes 2 glasses

1 banana
2 tbsp crunchy peanut butter
1 cup chocolate milk (use your preferred milk)
¼ cup Greek yoghurt
1 tbsp ground hazelnuts

We all know that chocolate is a great energy food so we should include at least one chocolate smoothie in our collection. This is truly the easiest post-workout smoothie to make, and if you are a chocolate lover then you will really enjoy this one. Any other kind of nut butter can be used instead of peanut butter.

Benefits: This chocolate smoothie helps the body to recover from a workout or any other strenuous activity. Aside from helping to hydrate the body, milk and yoghurt also provide us with lots of minerals, nutrients, carbohydrates and proteins to replace what is lost during exercising. Nuts are high in protein and will keep you feeling full for longer. The hazelnuts and peanut butter combine well to flavour this smoothie.

Handy hints: Peanuts are classified as both a 'grain legume' and an 'oil crop', but not as nuts! In many parts of the world peanuts are boiled and then eaten as a savoury dish or as street food. Interestingly, boiled peanuts have four times the antioxidants of raw or roasted peanuts because the process draws antioxidants from their shells.

Good manners and kindness are always in fashion.

Dairy-free smoothies

According to the Physicians Committee for Responsible Medicine, which maintains a website* that is really worth a visit for anyone interested in the non-dairy sources of calcium and magnesium, lactose intolerance is more widespread than was originally thought.

According to this source, 'Lactose intolerance is the inability to digest the milk sugar lactose, causing gastrointestinal symptoms of flatulence, bloating, cramps, and diarrhoea in some individuals.'

From recent research it is now clear that around '75 percent of the world's population . . . lose their lactase enzymes after weaning.' In reality, it is only among the majority of adults in, or originating from, Northern Europe and some Mediterranean populations that we can expect to find widespread lactose tolerance.

So, for more and more people around the world, dairy free is the way to be! For many it is a necessity, while for a growing number it is just a healthier option.

I hope the following non-dairy smoothies will prove to be both healthy and tasty.

* Source: *http://www.pcrm.org/health/diets/vegdiets/what-is-lactose-intolerance*

Coconut pumpkin

A beautiful autumn smoothie that you could have either cold or warmed up. Sprinkle roasted coconut over the top. It's both filling and bursting with flavour.

Benefits: Although a fruit, butternut squash (butternut) is used largely as a vegetable. It has a sweet, nutty taste, similar to that of a pumpkin. When one compares the nutritional values of pumpkin and butternut the latter comes out on top. Butternut has a much higher calorie density, three times the carbohydrate loading, and four times the dietary fibre.

Handy hints: Soak the cashews and dates in hot water for five minutes for easier blending.

Ingredients
Makes 2 glasses

½ cup coconut milk (or similar non-dairy milk)
½ cup pumpkin or butternut purée
1 small golden apple, peeled and diced
¼ cup chopped dates
¼ cup cashew nuts
½ tsp vanilla extract
2 tbsp coconut butter
¾ tsp cinnamon
Roasted coconut for sprinkling

'Dyspepsia is the remorse of a guilty stomach.' *A. Kerr*

Cherry-berry

Ingredients
Makes 2 glasses

1 cup cherry juice
1 cup silken tofu
½ cup dairy-free plain yoghurt
2 tbsp honey

Tart cherry juice has a high concentration of antioxidants and is promoted as a natural juice that helps to ease post-exercise pain, alleviate insomnia and combat gout.

Benefits: Tart cherry juice is antioxidant-rich, but cherries seem to be very helpful in other ways too. They contain high levels of melatonin, the 'sleeping hormone', which helps you to sleep better. Cherries seem to lower the levels of uric acid in the body, bringing relief to gout sufferers. Cherries also have properties that fight inflammation, thereby easing painful joints. Tofu is described as being naturally gluten-free, low in calories, cholesterol-free and an excellent source of protein, iron, and calcium. The soya bean is the main ingredient of tofu and is a complete source of dietary protein, providing all of the essential amino acids needed in the diet. Tofu is considered very beneficial for women during menopause because of the isoflavones, a type of phytochemical, that it contains.

Handy hints: The National Honey Board recommends adding honey to your bottle of water for an energy boost during workouts.

'You are what you eat – so don't be fast, cheap, easy or fake.'
Unknown

Coconut mango

Mango is the national fruit of India and, as we said earlier, is known as 'the king of fruits'. It is luscious and sweet, but also full of life-giving nutrients and vitamins. When combined with the subtle taste of coconut milk and vanilla it results in a truly special smoothie.

Benefits: Besides being tasty, mango is loaded with an array of vitamins to ensure your overall health. It is also low in fat, sodium and cholesterol, but eating too much mango can also make you gain weight. Mango has a high calorie count per gram and it also contains starch that is converted into sugar. It is therefore a good food for those who struggle to put on weight. It is also good for those of us who don't. Lemons are good for so many things, and when you enjoy one in a smoothie you hardly notice the acidity. They are rich in antioxidants, which help to balance the body's pH, bring down a fever and prepare the digestive tract for food.

Handy hints: Mixing lemon juice with honey can help alleviate the discomfort that comes from a nasty sore throat. If you add fresh sage it will help a cough.

Ingredients
Makes 2 glasses

1 large mango, diced
1 cup coconut milk
1 tbsp lemon juice
1 tbsp coconut oil
½ cup yoghurt
1½ tsp vanilla extract
Lemon zest for sprinkling

'Worries go down better with soup.'
Jewish proverb

Strawberry sweet

Ingredients
Makes 2 glasses

½ cup fresh
strawberries
½ banana
¼ cup dates
½ cup dairy-free
strawberry yoghurt
1 tbsp ground almonds
1 tbsp fresh lemon juice
½ tsp finely grated
lemon zest

'The most
remarkable thing
about my mother is
that for thirty years
she served the
family nothing
but leftovers. The
original meal has
never been found.'
Calvin Trillin

Strawberry and banana always make a good smoothie: it doesn't seem to matter what you add to it. Sometimes the strawberries can be a bit tart and the sweetness of the dates and yoghurt counteracts that. Frozen strawberries work equally well.

Benefits: Strawberries are an excellent source of vitamins C and K, as well as providing a good dose of fibre, folic acid, manganese and potassium. They also contain significant amounts of phytonutrients and flavonoids, which make them that bright red. A 100g serving of strawberries contains about 32 calories, 7.7g of carbs, 0.3g of fat and 2g of fibre – a sweet way to stay full. Dates are good for gaining weight – for those rare individuals who need help! They are also a good source of energy and fibre, making them an excellent pre-workout food.

Handy hints: Dates that are soaked overnight will help relieve someone suffering from constipation.

Avo-creamed

In this smoothie the mild taste of the avocado is beautifully complemented by the light tartness of the yoghurt. This is a quick, simple meal in a glass.

Benefits: Avocado has a high fat content but is a great way to add some healthy fat to your diet, and the combined fat and protein levels in this avocado-and-yoghurt smoothie will give you a good feeling of satiety. Botanically the avocado is a fruit: more specifically, a large berry with a single seed inside. A 2013 study found that US avocado consumers had a better overall diet quality and nutrient levels and a lower risk of metabolic syndrome than non-consumers.

Handy hints: Store avocados at room temperature, keeping in mind that they can take four or five days to ripen. This process can be speeded up by putting them in a paper bag along with an apple or a banana.

Ingredients
Makes 1 glass

1 avocado
¼ cup plain dairy-free yoghurt
Pinch of cayenne
Pinch of salt
3 ice cubes

'A nickel's worth of goulash beats a five-dollar can of vitamins.'
Martin H. Fischer

Grapefruit arrest

Ingredients
Makes 1 glass

1 large pear
½ large grapefruit, peeled
4 kale leaves
Small handful parsley
A few ice cubes

'We are living in a world today where lemonade is made from artificial flavours and furniture polish is made from real lemons.'
Alfred E. Newman

A very refreshing smoothie with a distinct grapefruit taste.

Benefits: Pears are usually sweet, mild and juicy to the taste. A pear's mildness makes it a fairly safe first fruit to introduce to babies. The pectin in pears is diuretic and has a mild laxative effect, which helps to keep you regular. Pectin also helps to lower cholesterol levels. Pears can be pretty amazing in boosting the immune system. Drink a glass if you feel a cold coming, or to lower a fever and ease a sore throat. Grapefruit is high in vitamin C. It cleanses the lymphatic system and stimulates fat burning. The dietary insoluble fibre pectin, also found in grapefruit, helps to protect the colon. Kale contains all the nutrients, minerals and vitamins of rich leafy vegetables and adds to the goodness of this smoothie. The taste of grapefruit dominates this smoothie.

Handy hints: Parsley has a slight peppery taste, making it a great addition to a salad or soup, but it is also an effective breath freshener when you chew it raw.

Peachy oats

A real summer smoothie that makes you taste the sunshine. Almonds are good brain food and oats provide a slow energy release for longer satiety. You may increase the amount of almond milk if the mixture is too thick.

Ingredients
Makes 2 glasses

2 peaches
1 banana
2 ripe apricots
¼ cup rolled oats
½ cup almond milk
1 tbsp crushed almonds

Benefits: Peaches will give you a quick energy boost. They are also low in fat, cholesterol-free and a good vitamin C and vitamin A booster. Vitamin C is an antioxidant that protects the skin. Vitamin A helps to protect your eyesight, an especially important factor as we grow older. The banana, milk and oats fill you up. Besides being good for energy, bananas also contain tryptophan, serotonin and norepinephrine, which help to balance our moods. Oats have a low glycaemic load and are a slow-release energy food that keeps you going for longer.

Handy hints: Among nuts almonds are the most nutritionally dense. This means that for every calorie you consume you get more vitamins and minerals than from any other nut.

Good food is good mood.

Beet health

Ingredients
Makes 2 glasses

4 medium-sized
beetroots, boiled for
easier blending
1 cup tofu or plain
non-dairy yoghurt
(made from coconut
milk, almond milk, or
soya milk)
2 cups baby spinach
leaves

'We should look for
someone to eat
and drink with
before looking for
something to eat
and drink.'
Epicurus

This smoothie has a pretty dark colour, but the
combination with spinach makes it a nutritious and
unusual drink. If you feel that the texture is too
dense you can thin it with some milk or beetroot
water.

Benefits: We have already established the
excellent nutritional credentials of beetroot and
spinach, but what about those of tofu? Tofu is an
excellent source of protein, containing all eight
essential amino acids. In addition to which, it is
a very good source of iron, calcium, manganese,
selenium, phosphorus, magnesium, copper, zinc
and vitamin B1.

Handy hints: When opened all firm tofu should
be rinsed, then covered with water and kept in a
fridge container. To keep it fresh for up to a week,
change its water often.

Summary breeze

A minty tropical smoothie that should be served chilled. The fruits must be ripe to benefit fully from their rich flavours. Both the mango and persimmon thicken this smoothie, and it can be diluted slightly with some fizzy lemonade to enhance the flavours.

Ingredients
Makes 2 glasses

5 very ripe persimmons
2 small green apples
½ peeled lemon
½ stringless mango
1 peeled tangerine/clementine
20 mint leaves
3 ice cubes per glass

Benefits: You may not be too familiar with persimmons, so let me provide a bit of background. Like the tomato, persimmons are actually berries, and should be eaten when ripe, at which time they are very sweet. Interestingly, when compared with apples they have higher levels of dietary fibre, sodium, potassium, magnesium, calcium, iron and manganese, but lower levels of copper and zinc. They are also a source of vitamin C.

Handy hints: Fresh mango freezes well, which then makes it available for that out-of-season smoothie.

'After dinner sit a while, and after supper walk a mile.'
English saying

Chocolate cashew date

Ingredients
Makes 3 glasses

1 cup cashews
1 cup pitted dates
¼ cup cocoa powder
¾ cup boiling water
1 cup coconut milk
½ block silken tofu
Ice cubes

This is a complete meal. Nutritious and delicious! Cocoa, cashew and coconut make a wonderful drink. Tofu thickens this smoothie and adds a creaminess to the taste. Use ice cubes to chill the hot cocoa.

Place the cashews, dates, cocoa, and water in the blender. Cover and let the mixture rest for five minutes to soften cashews and dates before blending.

Benefits: Cocoa helps to stimulate the feel-good chemicals in the brain known as serotonin and dopamine. A tablespoon of cocoa powder contains about 12 calories, but this increases when you add sugar to sweeten it, since a teaspoon of sugar contains 16 calories. Coconut milk is lactose-free, so it can be used as a milk substitute by those with lactose intolerance. In fact, it is an indispensable ingredient in Asian cooking. Coconut is a relatively complete food that provides almost all the daily requirement of essential minerals, vitamins, and energy for an average-sized person.

Handy hints: Cashew-nut allergy is a common hypersensitivity condition. The allergy symptoms may range from simple skin itching (hives) to anaphylactic shock manifestations, including breathing difficulty, abdominal pain, vomiting, and diarrhoea.

'Strawberries are the angels of the earth – innocent and sweet with green leafy wings reaching heavenward.'
Terri Guillemets

Better health smoothies

For most of you, your interest in juicing and smoothie making is inspired by a desire to enjoy optimum health. Like me you are committed to putting the best stuff in, in order to get the best stuff out!

For you it is not just about taste and appearance – it's about goodness. Goodness for yourself and your loved ones. Goodness that will last. If that is how you see things, then the following set of recipes, the last in our smoothie section, is just what you are looking for.

If you enjoy them – and I am sure you will – then take the time to share them with your family and your friends. Let them in on the secret too!

Green and spicy

This is a thick, spicy green smoothie that includes the fresh taste of cucumber and herbs. There are a few ingredients that act as a thickener, making your smoothie creamier and more substantial than a juice. To achieve this I like using yoghurt, coconut milk, and fruits like mango, apricot or banana, for example. Remember that, as a rule of thumb, a smoothie should not taste raw.

Experiment with the quantities of herbs and spices until you find the combination that suits you.

Benefits: A good detoxing juice uses fruits, veggies, herbs and spices that function as diuretics, to cleanse and replenish. Both cucumber and celery have this effect and help rid the body of water. The fibre in the other fruits helps to cleanse the body too, flushing out nasty toxins. Cayenne pepper heats up the body and helps to make it alkaline. Tumeric helps to keep your liver healthy.

Handy hints: Tumeric is known as the 'golden' spice of India and when you cook with it everything turns a lovely orange-yellowy shade. Fresh turmeric looks much like fresh ginger.

Ingredients
Makes 2 glasses

1 cup spinach or kale leaves
½ cup chopped cucumber
½ cup chopped celery
1 pear
1 banana (preferably frozen)
1 cup coconut milk
6 fresh mint leaves or a handful of coriander (cilantro) or parsley
½ tbsp fresh lemon juice
2cm chunk ginger
A pinch of cayenne, cinnamon and turmeric

'It's more fun to talk with someone who doesn't use long, difficult words, but rather short, easy words like, "What about lunch?" '
Winnie the Pooh

Light green

I enjoy having Greek yoghurt in a smoothie mixed with fruit or veggies. In this case the combination of yoghurt, lemon and ginger makes this a very simple smoothie for detoxing.

Ingredients
Makes 2 glasses

1 cup Greek yoghurt
1 banana
1 pear
2 cups spinach
1 tbsp fresh lemon juice
1 tbsp freshly grated ginger

Benefits: The probiotics, calcium and protein in natural yoghurt provide a good base for a detoxing smoothie. The banana and pear provide fibre that helps to cleanse the body. Pectin, a soluble fibre in bananas, helps to keep you regular, thereby preventing constipation. Both lemon and ginger help to cleanse the body, while lemon helps to alkalise the body and clean the liver.

Handy hints: Drinking a glass of warm water with lemon juice will help to reduce pain and inflammation in the joints and knees, as lemon juice is known to dissolve uric acid. Caution should be observed when drinking lemon juice because it can be damaging to our teeth in a concentrated form.

'Food for thought is no substitute for the real thing.'
Walk Kelly

Green delish

This is a really tasty, must-try smoothie. Have one soon!

Benefits: Celery helps to remove all the excess fluid in the body and reduce its overall acidity. Green apples do not have such a high sugar content, and apples are generally high in soluble fibre and help to cleanse the subcutaneous tissue where the body stores fat. They also help to clear the body of toxins. Mint is also a good diuretic that increases the flushing out of toxins and helps to soothe the digestive system. Oranges and lemons are rich in vitamin C, dietary fibre and other minerals. Lemons, as mentioned previously, are powerful detoxifiers and excellent liver cleansers.

Handy hints: Mint is well-known as a breath freshener or palate cleanser, but is also often included before the main course so the food will digest comfortably.

Ingredients
Makes 2 glasses

1 orange, peeled
1 medium banana, peeled
1 green apple
½ lime
3 stalks celery
Small sprig mint
1 glass almond milk

'True happiness comes from the joy of deeds well done, the zest of creating things new.'
Antoine de Saint-Exupery

Friendly berries

Ingredients
Makes 2 glasses

2 cups mixed berries
1 cup coconut milk
½ cup water
¼ cup rolled oats
¼ cup mint

Besides being a healthy, tasty treat, berries are also good when used as part of a detox regimen because of all the antioxidants and fibre they contain. This is also an excellent breakfast smoothie.

Benefits: Antioxidants play an important role in protecting the body from various diseases. Vitamin A and vitamin C help to maintain and protect the body's immune system. Oats fill you up and provide energy to keep you going. We need much more water than we usually take in so that our bodies can be properly hydrated. Coconut milk provides healthy fat, making this a very satisfying smoothie even though it is being used as a detoxing drink.

Handy hints: Having a handful of berries every day can provide the body with all the antioxidants that it needs.

'He that eats till he is sick must fast till he is well.'
English proverb

Green-it

Kale is the new spinach, and as such you should make sure you're eating some on a semi-regular basis. A smoothie makes a great vehicle for upping your kale intake, since the curly kind of kale can be a bit much to munch on.

Benefits: All edible green leaves of any vegetable are packed with life-giving and cleansing nutrients and vitamins. Steam the leaves lightly before blending. Coconut milk provides healthy fat and protein, which keeps you full for longer and hydrates the body. Apples contain pectin, which helps to remove toxins from the intestines and other systems of the body. Apples are also high in soluble fibre, which aids the digestive process.

Handy hints: An apple a day keeps the doctor away. Apples also reduce tooth decay by cleaning one's teeth and killing off bacteria, and are often served after a meal – but for the full benefit don't peel the apple! The fibre in the skin is essential in this process. However, this is no substitute for brushing your teeth, as the sugars and acid in apples may cause damage to the enamel almost as bad as plaque.

Ingredients
Makes 2 glasses

1 cup tender kale leaves
1 cup tender beetroot leaves
1 apple, peeled
1 cup coconut milk

'The spirit cannot endure the body when overfed, but, if underfed, the body cannot endure the spirit.'
St Francis de Sales

Water

Water-based drinks

Although most drinks here are not prepared using either a juice extractor or a blender, this final category of juices deserves 'honourable mention'. To make them you won't need to shop around for a basketful of ingredients. None of them requires much fuss to put together and they won't be much good as meal replacements either.

Most of them need to be drunk quickly – after all, they are meant to be 'shots'. Why not be creative and dream up a few of your own?

Thanks for joining me on this journey. I hope you have been able to take as much pleasure out of this book as I have had in writing it for you.

Lemon flush

I think lemon and water was my first introduction to a water-based cleansing juice. It is probably also the most well-known and accepted health drink. Enjoy it first thing in the morning; it will clean out your system and prepare it for food.

Benefits: Lemon juice is relatively low in calories but high in vitamin C, which is helpful for making collagen. This is a protein that should be abundant in your skin and which provides some natural sun protection. The juice is also a potent antioxidant and helps your body absorb the iron found in plant-based foods like lentils and spinach.

Handy hints: Because exposure to concentrated lemon juice erodes tooth enamel some people prefer to drink their lemon drinks through a straw, which minimises the juice's contact with your teeth.

Ingredients
Makes 1 glass of warm water

1 glass of warm water Add a few drops of lemon juice to the water – which you can increase according to individual taste, but always make sure it is well-diluted.

'A good cook knows it's not what's on the table that matters, it's what's in the chairs.'
wadulifashions.com

第16帖 A面

The ginger shot

Ingredients
Makes 1 shot glass

½ unpeeled apple
1cm chunk ginger

I was introduced to a ginger shot by my friend, Viv. I love it first thing in the morning. It wakes me up and warms up my body. Ginger is good for so many things, including your immune system in the morning. It is very simple and open to some variation of the ingredients but the ginger is not negotiable. Gulp, don't sip, because this can be a potent 'brew'. Whew!

Benefits: The use of ginger in any of its forms (grated, peeled, sliced, etc) will be beneficial to your system. For example, a little fresh ginger before a meal can 'inspire' your appetite and kickstart your digestive juices. It is also regarded as a facilitator for the absorption of certain essential nutrients into the system. Some people find that ginger helps clear the sinuses, curb flatulence and help cope with nausea.

Handy hints: Ginger appears to be very effective in controlling menstrual pain when used at the beginning of the menstrual period. Some sources suggest that it can be as effective at this as drugs such as mefenamic acid and ibuprofen.

'I like a cook who smiles out loud when he tastes his own work.'
Underwood Spreads

Ginger/lemon/cayenne

This classic juice shot uses simple well-known kitchen cupboard ingredients with lots of health benefits. Both ginger and lemon aid digestion and detoxify the body. Together they protect the immune system and both cayenne and ginger are known to help reduce joint inflammation and pain. You may want to follow up this 'shot' with a glass of water.

Juice the lemon and ginger. Pour into a glass and sprinkle with cayenne. Down it quickly.

Ingredients
Makes 1 shot glass

Ginger (start with a 1cm chunk)
½-1 lemon
Cayenne

Benefits: The benefits of this potent shot are as mentioned in the last two recipes. The use of cayenne pepper (capsicum) is worth noting, however. This herb has many benefits similar to those of ginger, such as helping us cope with an upset stomach, cramps, nausea and flatulence. In addition to this it is regarded as helpful in improving circulation and reducing excessive blood clotting and cholesterol.

Handy hints: Some people apply capsicum to the skin to relieve the pain caused by shingles and muscle spasms, and as a gargle in cases of laryngitis. It has also been used by some to discourage thumb-sucking and nail-biting.

'A man may be a pessimistic determinist before lunch and an optimistic believer in the will's freedom after it.'
Aldous Huxley

Ginger/lemon/honey

Ingredients
Makes 1 quarter-glass

½ lemon
¼ glass hot water
Ginger
Honey

When you are feeling fluey or your energies are flagging take a few minutes to make and drink this one.

Grate a tablespoon of ginger into a quarter-glass of hot water and steep for about 5 minutes, then drain. Juice half a lemon into it and add honey to taste. Have it as hot as possible.

Benefits: Adding honey to the ginger and lemon juice brings further benefits. One tablespoon of raw honey is said to contain 64 calories and it is fat-free, cholesterol-free and contains no sodium. It is composed of approximately 80% carbohydrates and 18% water, with the balance being made up of 2% vitamins, minerals and amino acids. Honey is believed to be as effective as dextromethorphan, the common cough suppressant, found in various cough mixtures. A 2012 study reported in the journal *Pediatrics* found that 'children between the ages of 1 and 5 with night-time cough due to colds coughed less frequently when they received two teaspoons of honey 30 minutes before bed' *(www.medicaldaily.com)*.

Handy hints: Honey contaminated by spores of the *Clostridium botulinum* bacterium may lead to infant botulism that results in muscle weakness and respiratory problems. The Mayo Clinic recommends that honey not be given to infants under 12 months of age.

'Cooking is love made edible.'
Michael Mullan

Sip by sip

A simple and easy way to detox and cleanse your body daily is by sipping water that is flavoured with real fruits. For this, use fruits that are well associated with weight loss, cleansing and the improvement of digestion.

Fill the water jug or water bottle at your desk with slices of grapefruit, lemon, cucumber or mint leaves and sip throughout the day. Alternatively, you can brighten your day by using a variety of berries instead.

Ingredients
Makes 1 jug

Grapefruit, lemon, cucumber, or mint leaves

Calories (Noun):
Tiny creatures that live in your closet and sew your clothes a little bit tighter every night.

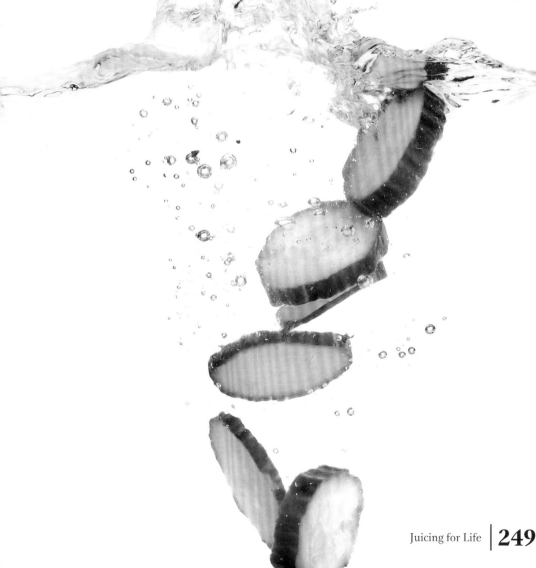

Simple water

Ingredients
Makes as much water as you want

H_2O

I am constantly amazed at how few people drink water, or enough water, simply because they don't understand that water is the number-one health drink created especially to hydrate and cleanse all living things. The human body is made up of almost 70% water, which should constantly be replenished in order for our bodies and minds to function optimally.

Pure water still remains nature's wonder liquid. Water flushes harmful toxins out of the body, it energises the body and mind and it keeps the body machinery hydrated so that we function optimally. If we are eating, resting and exercising properly, an adequate water intake will also help us lose weight.

According to a report by the Institute of Medicine referred to by the Mayo Clinic, 'An adequate intake (AI) for men is roughly about 13 cups (3 litres) of total beverages a day. The AI for women is about 9 cups (2.2 litres) of total beverages a day' *(www.mayoclinic.org)*.

Foody facts

Food	Vitamins, minerals and phytonutrients	Potential benefits	Precautions
Almonds	Calcium, copper, fibre, folate (DFE), iron, magnesium, niacin (vitamin B3), phosphorus, potassium, riboflavin (vitamin B2), sodium, thiamin (vitamin B1), zinc, vitamins A (IU), B6, E (alpha-tocopherol)	Lowers cholesterol, reduces risk of colon cancer and heart disease	Allergic reaction

See pages: 162, 166, 177, 181, 189, 214, 221, 222, 233

| Apples | Beta-carotene, calcium, fibre, folate (vitamin B9), iron, lutein and zeaxanthin, magnesium, manganese, niacin (vitamin B3), pantothenic acid (vitamin B5), phosphorus, potassium, riboflavin (vitamin B2), sodium, thiamin (vitamin B1), vitamins A (equiv.), B6, C, E, K | Improves neurological health, prevents dementia, reduces risk of stroke, lowers levels of bad cholesterol, reduces risk of diabetes and breast cancer | Seeds contain cyanide; acidity of apples can damage teeth when snacked on apart from meals |

See pages: 47, 48, 51, 52, 55, 56, 59, 60, 64, 67, 68, 71, 72, 75, 76, 79, 80, 83, 84, 87, 91, 92, 95, 96, 99, 103, 104, 107, 108, 111, 115, 116, 119, 120, 124, 127, 136, 139, 140, 144, 154, 185, 205, 209, 225, 233, 237, 242

| Apricots | Alpha-carotene and beta-carotene, calcium, chloride, choline, cryptoxanthin, copper, fibre, folate (DFE), iron, lutein and zeaxanthin, magnesium, manganese, pantothenic acid, phosphorus, potassium, selenium, sodium, zinc, vitamins A, B1, B2, B3, B6, E, K | Protection against free radical damage and inflammation; protection of eyesight | Sulfites used to preserve dried apricots can cause allergic reactions, particularly with asthmatics |

See pages: 161, 221

| Avocados | Beta-carotene, beta-sitosterol, fibre, folate, lutein and zeaxanthin, magnesium, niacin, riboflavin, omega-3s, pantothenic acid, potassium, vitamins B6, C, E, K | Protection of heart, eyesight and digestion; protection against osteoporosis, cancer, depression and chronic disease; natural detoxification and good for foetus in pregnant women | If taking blood-thinners, don't dramatically change level of vitamin K consumption |

See pages: 169, 174, 198, 217

| Bananas | Fibre, folate, iron, magnesium, manganese, niacin, riboflavin, potassium, vitamins A, B6, C | Reduces blood pressure and risk of asthma, cancer, heart disease, strokes, and kidney stones; beneficial for sufferers of diabetes and diarrhoea; preserves memory and boosts mood | If taking beta-blockers or your kidneys aren't fully functional, consume in moderation |

See pages: 154, 157, 158, 162, 169, 170, 173, 177, 186, 189, 190, 194, 197, 206, 214, 221, 229, 230, 233

Food	Vitamins, minerals and phytonutrients	Potential benefits	Precautions
Beetroot *See pages: 75, 80, 87, 104, 112, 116, 132, 144, 185, 205, 222, 237*	Betaine, calcium, choline, copper, dietary nitrate, fibre, folate, iron, magnesium, manganese, pantothenic acid, phosphorus, potassium, riboflavin, selenium, thiamin, zinc, vitamins A, B6, C	Boosts digestion, exercise performance, complexion, hair, energy and weight loss; protects against dementia, inflammation, high blood pressure and cardiovascular conditions	If improperly stored, nitrates may be converted to nitrites, which can be harmful; take care if using nitrite medications
Blackberries *See pages: 88, 149, 170*	Beta-carotene, calcium, catechins, copper, cyanidins, ellagic acid, fibre, folate, folic acid, gallic acid, iron, kaempferol, lutein and zeaxanthin, magnesium, manganese, niacin, pantothenic acid, pelargonidins, potassium, pyridoxine, quercetin, riboflavin, salicylic acid, selenium, sodium, tannin, thiamin, xylitol, zinc, vitamins A, C, E, K	Steadies blood sugar levels; may protect against cancer, infections, inflammation and neurological diseases	Allergic reaction (rare)
Broccoli *See pages: 51, 63, 71, 72, 84, 123*	Fibre, folate, potassium, sulforaphane, vitamins A, C, K	Contributes to decreased risk of chronic diseases, obesity, diabetes, heart disease, and some cancers; reduces wrinkles; improves bone health, digestion and natural detoxification	If taking blood-thinners, don't dramatically change level of vitamin K consumption
Butternut squash *See page: 209*	Fibre, folate, magnesium, manganese, niacin, pantothenic acid, potassium, thiamin, vitamins A, B6, C, E	Contributes to decreased risk of asthma, cancer, obesity, diabetes and heart disease; promotes immune function, healthy complexion, increased energy, weight loss; lowers blood pressure	If taking beta-blockers or your kidneys aren't fully functional, consume in moderation
Cabbage *See pages: 52, 59, 119*	Apigenin, beta-carotene, calcium, choline, fibre, folate, kaempferol, lutein and zeaxanthin, manganese, potassium, quercetin, sulforaphane, thiamin, vitamins C, K	Contributes to reduced risk of obesity, heart disease, diabetes, cancer and harmful effects of radiation therapy; promotes healthy complexion, increased energy, lower weight, immunity and digestion	If taking blood-thinners, don't dramatically change level of vitamin K consumption

Food	Vitamins, minerals and phytonutrients	Potential benefits	Precautions
Carrots	Beta-carotene, calcium, fibre, folate, iron, magnesium, phosphorus, potassium, zinc, vitamins A, C, K	Protects against eyesight deterioration, cancer and cardiovascular disease	Overconsumption of vitamin A can be toxic, but dietary intake alone is unlikely to lead to these levels
See pages: 47, 63, 64, 72, 75, 87, 91, 100, 112, 116, 119, 124, 128, 132, 139, 143, 198, 205			
Cashews	Calcium, copper, fibre, folate, magnesium, manganese, oleic acid, potassium, pyridoxine, sodium, thiamin, vitamin E	Decreases risk of cardiovascular diseases, gallstones, tooth decay, gum disease, high blood pressure (if unsalted), fatigue and muscle spasms; promotes weight control (if used in moderation!) and healthy bones, connective tissues, skin and hair	Allergic reactions: particularly anaphylaxis and head pain, among others
See pages: 166, 173, 182, 201, 209, 226			
Cauliflower	Calcium, fibre, folate, iron, magnesium, manganese, niacin, pantothenic acid, phosphorus, potassium, riboflavin, thiamin, vitamins B6, C, K	Contributes to decreased risk of obesity, diabetes, heart disease and cancer; promotes healthy complexion and bones, good memory, increased energy, lower weight and good digestion	High quantities may cause bloating in some people; if taking blood-thinners, don't dramatically change level of vitamin K consumption
See pages: 75, 140, 185			
Cayenne pepper	Calcium, capsaicin, flavonoids, iron, magnesium, manganese, niacin, phosphorus, potassium, selenium, sodium, zinc, vitamins A, B6, C, E	Slight pain-relieving benefit; can burn calories and suppress appetite, and treat psoriasis and cluster headaches in topical application	Avoid if taking ACE inhibitors or stomach acid reducers; wash hands straight after use, and avoid contact with eyes
See pages: 52, 111, 119, 169, 174, 198, 217, 229, 245			
Celery	Dihydrostilbenoids, fibre, flavones, flavonols, folate, furanocoumarins, phenolic acids, phytosterols, potassium, vitamins A, C, K	Slight evidence seeds may lower blood pressure; reduces risk of cancer and age-related degeneration of vision	Allergic reactions (rare), including anaphylactic shock
See pages: 47, 51, 59, 60, 64, 71, 72, 75, 76, 79, 80, 84, 96, 104, 107, 108, 111, 115, 116, 119, 120, 123, 124, 127, 131, 135, 140, 178, 229, 233			

Food	Vitamins, minerals and phytonutrients	Potential benefits	Precautions
Cherries *See page: 210*	Anthocyanin glycosides, beta-carotene, calcium, copper, fibre, folates, iron, lutein and zeaxanthin, magnesium, manganese, melatonin, niacin, phosphorus, potassium, pyridoxine, riboflavin, thiamin, zinc, vitamins A, C	Can counteract inflammation and help to alleviate gout, arthritis, fibromyalgia and sports injuries; eases neurosis, insomnia and headaches; helps regulate heart rate and blood pressure	
Chia seeds *See pages: 104, 190, 197*	Calcium, copper, fibre, iron, magnesium, manganese, omega-3s, phosphorus, potassium, zinc	Can decrease prevalence of diverticulitis, assist weight loss, lower blood and cholesterol levels, and decrease risk of cardiovascular disease, diabetes, cancer, and obesity	Mix chia seeds with another food or liquid before swallowing
Cinnamon *See pages: 99, 150, 153, 157, 173, 186, 189, 190, 209, 229*	Beta-carotene, beta-cryptoxanthin, calcium, copper, coumarin, fibre, folates, iron, lutein and zeaxanthin, lycopene, magnesium, manganese, niacin, pantothenic acid, phosphorus, potassium, pyridoxine, riboflavin, sodium, thiamin, zinc, vitamins A, C, E, K	Used to treat muscle spasms, vomiting, diarrhoea, infections and loss of appetite; may be of benefit in diabetes, HIV, multiple sclerosis, chronic wounds, and prevention of Alzheimer's disease	Sensitive persons may suffer increased risk of liver damage due to coumarin
Clementine *See pages: 181, 225*	Fibre, folate, potassium, vitamins A, B6, C	Reduces risk of infections, Alzheimer's disease and cognitive decline; beneficial in pregnant women; maintains healthy blood pressure, heart, digestion, hair and skin	
Cocoa *See pages: 154, 194, 226*	Caffeine, copper, fibre, flavonoids (incl. flavonols), iron, magnesium, phosphorus	Benefits nervous and cardiovascular systems; supports healthy bones and cognitive functioning, and boosts blood flow to brain	Some persons may be sensitive to caffeine

Food	Vitamins, minerals and phytonutrients	Potential benefits	Precautions
Coconut	Calcium, fibre, iron, lauric acid, magnesium, phosphorus, selenium, sodium, vitamins B1, B3, B5, B6, C, E	May protect body from infections	Contains high level of saturated fatty acids: consume in moderation

See pages: 165, 173, 177, 185, 186, 198, 202, 209, 213, 222, 226, 229, 234, 237

Food	Vitamins, minerals and phytonutrients	Potential benefits	Precautions
Coriander	Beta-carotene, beta-cryptoxanthin, choline, folate, lutein and zeaxanthin, manganese, potassium, vitamins A, C, K	Antibacterial effect against salmonella; heavy metal chelation; contributes to decreased risk of obesity, diabetes and heart disease, and healthier hair and skin	

See pages: 72, 75, 181, 229

Food	Vitamins, minerals and phytonutrients	Potential benefits	Precautions
Cranberries	Calcium, fibre, folate (DFE), iron, magnesium, niacin, phosphorus, potassium, riboflavin, sodium, thiamin, zinc, vitamins A, B6, C, E, K	Prevents urinary tract infections and possibly tooth decay and gum disease; may also slow tumour progression and reduce risk of cardiovascular disease	Exercise caution if taking blood-thinning medication or you have a history of kidney stones

See pages: 153, 157, 169

Food	Vitamins, minerals and phytonutrients	Potential benefits	Precautions
Cucumber	Calcium, copper, fibre, folate, iron, magnesium, manganese, pantothenic acid, phosphorus, potassium, riboflavin, thiamin, zinc, vitamins A, B6, C, K	Used for hydration and to maintain bone health; when applied topically, decreases irritation, swelling and inflammation	Commercially grown cucumbers can be high in pesticides: wash thoroughly

See pages: 47, 48, 51, 56, 59, 60, 63, 67, 68, 71, 75, 76, 79, 80, 83, 84, 92, 107, 108, 111, 115, 119, 124, 127, 131, 132, 140, 144, 178, 229, 249

Food	Vitamins, minerals and phytonutrients	Potential benefits	Precautions
Dates 	Beta-carotene, calcium, copper, fibre, folates, iron, lutein and zeaxanthin, magnesium, manganese, niacin, pantothenic acid, phosphorus, potassium, pyridoxine, riboflavin, sodium, tannins, thiamin, zinc, vitamins A, K	Assists digestion; maintains vision; helps protect against several cancers and age-related macular degeneration; May benefit bones and teeth, muscle contraction, blood clotting, nerve impulse conduction, and regulation of heart rate and blood pressure	Allergic reaction (rare)

See pages: 150, 153, 161, 162, 194, 209, 214, 226

Food	Vitamins, minerals and phytonutrients	Potential benefits	Precautions
Garlic	Allicin precursors, beta-carotene, calcium, copper, fibre, folates, iron, lutein and zeaxanthin, magnesium, manganese, niacin, pantothenic acid, phosphorus, potassium, pyridoxine, riboflavin,	Decreases risk of coronary artery disease, peripheral vascular disease and stroke; reduces risk of some cancers; protects	Avoid if taking anticoagulants, as allicin acts as blood-thinner

Food	Vitamins, minerals and phytonutrients	Potential benefits	Precautions

selenium, sodium, thiamin, zinc, vitamins A, C, E, K

See pages: 48, 72

against osteoarthritis, high cholesterol and blood pressure, and alcohol-induced liver injury

---

Ginger

Calcium, fibre, folate, iron, magnesium, niacin, phosphorus, potassium, riboflavin, sodium, zinc, vitamins B6, C

See pages: 47, 51, 55, 59, 72, 75, 83, 91, 92, 104, 107, 111, 115, 124, 127, 139, 140, 143, 166, 181, 185, 198, 205, 229, 230, 242, 245, 246

Relieves gastrointestinal irritation, nausea, some types of pain and inflammation; stimulates saliva and bile production, and suppresses gastric contractions and movement of food through GI tract

May exacerbate acid reflux in some people

Grapefruit

Calcium, choline, copper, fibre, folate, lycopene, magnesium, manganese, niacin, pantothenic acid, phosphorus, potassium, riboflavin, thiamin, zinc, vitamins A, C, E

See pages: 76, 120, 128, 135, 218, 249

May protect against asthma, cancer, high blood pressure, stroke and heart disease; improves digestion, skin texture and hydration; may assist weight loss

Avoid when taking certain medications, including statins, calcium channel blockers and psychiatric medication; take caution if prone to heartburn or if kidneys are not fully functional

---

Grapes

Fibre, folate, iron, lutein and zeaxanthin, myricetin, polyphenols, potassium, quercetin, vitamins A, C

See pages: 92, 95

Helps to prevent some types of cancer and cardiovascular disease; reduces blood pressure and constipation; may alleviate allergies and protect against diabetic neuropathy and retinopathy

If taking beta-blockers or your kidneys aren't fully functional, consume in moderation

---

Hazelnuts

Alpha-carotene, beta-carotene, calcium, copper, fibre, folate, iron, linoleic acid, lutein and zeaxanthin, magnesium, manganese, niacin, oleic acid, pantothenic acid, phosphorus, pyridoxine, riboflavin, potassium, selenium, thiamin, zinc, vitamins A, C, E, K

See page: 206

Helps to prevent coronary artery disease and strokes; beneficial for expectant mothers, and for maintaining skin and cell membranes

Allergic reactions are possible

Food	Vitamins, minerals and phytonutrients	Potential benefits	Precautions
Honey *See pages: 154, 166, 189, 210, 246*	Calcium, chlorine, iron, magnesium, phosphate, potassium, sodium	May help to prevent gastroesophageal reflux and radiation-induced dermatitis; may treat infantile gastroenteritis and allergies; fights infections	Consume in moderation
Kale *See pages: 51, 55, 63, 64, 68, 75, 80, 92, 107, 108, 111, 115, 136, 173, 174, 185, 186, 202, 218, 237*	Calcium, copper, iron, manganese, phosphorus, potassium, vitamins A, C, K	Improves blood glucose control in diabetics; lowers blood pressure and risk of cancer; improves bone health; lowers risk of developing asthma	If taking beta-blockers or your kidneys aren't fully functional, consume in moderation
Kiwi fruit *See pages: 60, 83, 88*	Choline, copper, fibre, folate, iron, magnesium, phosphorus, potassium, vitamins A, C, E, K	Maintains healthy skin tone and texture; reduces blood pressure; helps to prevent constipation, heart disease and stroke; improves sleep; decreases risk of obesity	If taking beta-blockers or your kidneys aren't fully functional, consume in moderation
Lemons *See pages: 47, 52, 59, 60, 63, 64, 68, 71, 75, 79, 80, 84, 87, 88, 92, 107, 108, 111, 112, 115, 123, 124, 131, 140, 144, 157, 174, 178, 198, 205, 213, 214, 225, 229, 230, 241, 245, 246, 249*	Calcium, copper, fibre, iron, magnesium, manganese, pantothenic acid, phosphorus, potassium, riboflavin, thiamin, vitamins B6, C	Decreases risk of stroke, obesity, heart disease, asthma, and diabetes; increases iron absorption; maintains healthy complexion; boosts the immune system	Sufferers of gastroesophageal reflux disease may experience heartburn if overconsumed; take water after lemon juice to protect tooth enamel
Lemongrass  *See page: 83*	Calcium, citronellal, copper, dipentene, folate, geranyl acetate, geraniol, iron, limonene, magnesium, manganese, methyl heptenone, myrcene, nerol, niacin, potassium, pyridoxine, riboflavin, selenium, sodium, thiamin, zinc, vitamins A, C	Anti-bacterial, anti-fungal and insecticidal; may relieve colitis, indigestion and gastroenteritis ailments	Oil can cause irritation in some individuals when applied topically
Lettuce	Beta-carotene, calcium, copper, fibre, folates, iron, lutein and zeaxanthin, magnesium, manganese, niacin, pantothenic acid, phosphorus, potassium, pyridoxine, riboflavin, sodium, thiamin,	Helps to prevent osteoporosis, iron-deficiency anaemia; reduces risk of cardiovascular diseases,	If commercially grown, wash before use to diminish intake of pesticides

Food	Vitamins, minerals and phytonutrients	Potential benefits	Precautions

| | zinc, vitamins A, C, E-a, K | age-related macular degeneration, Alzheimer's disease and some cancers; maintains healthy bones, mucous membranes and skin | |

See page: 185

| Mango | Beta-carotene, calcium, copper, fibre, folate, iron, potassium, zeaxanthin, vitamins A, B6, K | Helps to prevent age-related macular degeneration, constipation, heart disease, asthma, some types of cancer, and bone fracture; aids blood glucose control in diabetics; maintains healthy skin and hair | If taking beta-blockers or your kidneys aren't fully functional, consume in moderation; sufferers from latex allergy may experience cross-reaction |

See pages: 149, 161, 186, 213, 225

| Milk | Calcium, choline, magnesium, phosphorus, potassium, riboflavin, vitamins A, B6, B12, D (when fortified) | Aids muscle movement, growth and repair; aids sleep, learning and memory; maintains cellular membranes; helps to prevent depression | Lactose intolerance; milk allergy |

See pages: 150, 153, 154, 157, 161, 162, 170, 189, 190, 194, 206

| Mint  | Calcium, fibre, magnesium, menthol, phosphorus, potassium, rosmarinic acid, vitamins A, C | Relieves seasonal allergies, indigestion, irritable bowel syndrome and colds; when applied topically, calms and cools insect bites, rashes and other reactions | Do not take to soothe gastroesophageal reflux disease; use with caution if you have history of gallstones; do not apply topically to face of infant; avoid large doses of peppermint oil; avoid any amount of pure menthol |

See pages: 55, 67, 68, 100, 135, 136, 166, 174, 185, 202, 225, 229, 233, 234, 249

| Oats | Avenanthramides, carotenoids, fibre, flavonoids, magnesium, manganese, phosphorus, selenium, zinc, vitamin E | May reduce risk of coronary artery disease and colorectal cancer; may lower levels of cholesterol and blood pressure | Sufferers of gluten intolerance should be careful in case of cross-contamination with wheat |

See pages: 153, 154, 157, 190, 194, 197, 221, 234

Food	Vitamins, minerals and phytonutrients	Potential benefits	Precautions
Oranges  See pages: 79, 88, 100, 112, 115, 135, 182, 202, 233	Calcium, carotenoids, choline, copper, fibre, folate, iron, magnesium, manganese, niacin, pantothenic acid, phosphorus, potassium, riboflavin, selenium, thiamin, zeaxanthin, vitamins A, B6, C	May reduce risk of leukaemia in childhood and stroke in women; lowers blood pressure; reduces risk of heart disease and kidney stones; maintains healthy skin; aids blood glucose control in diabetics	Sufferers of gastroesophageal reflux disease may experience heartburn if overconsumed; if taking beta-blockers or your kidneys aren't fully functional, consume in moderation
Papaya See pages: 127, 166, 181, 182, 189	Alpha-carotene, beta-carotene, calcium, copper, fibre, folate, iron, lutein and zeaxanthin, lycopene, magnesium, niacin, pantothenic acid, phosphorus, potassium, pyridoxine, riboflavin, sodium, thiamin, zinc, vitamins A, C, E, K	May reduce risk of heart disease, diabetes and cancer; aids in digestion; improves blood glucose control in diabetics; lowers blood pressure; improves wound healing	Sufferers from latex allergy may experience cross-reaction
Parsley See pages: 48, 51, 55, 63, 76, 80, 139, 140, 218, 229	Apigenin, beta-carotene, calcium, copper, fibre, folate, iron, lutein and zeaxanthin, magnesium, manganese, myricetin, phosphorus, niacin, pantothenic acid, potassium, pyridoxine, riboflavin, sodium, thiamin, zinc, vitamins A, C, E, K	May help to prevent and even treat some cancers and diabetes; improves bone health	If taking blood-thinners, don't dramatically change level of vitamin K consumption
Peaches  See pages: 149, 150, 190, 221	Anthocyanins, catechins, chlorogenic acids, choline, copper, fibre, folate, iron, magnesium, manganese, niacin, phosphorus, potassium, quercetins, zinc, vitamins A, C, E, K	Helps prevent obesity-related diseases such as diabetes, metabolic syndrome and cardiovascular disease; may help to prevent some cancers; aids blood glucose control in diabetics; decreases risk of age-related macular degeneration	
Peanut butter See pages: 177, 206	Calcium, copper, folates, iron, magnesium, manganese, niacin, pantothenic acid, phosphorus, potassium, pyridoxine, resveratrol, riboflavin, selenium, sodium, thiamin, zinc, vitamin E	May reduce risk of heart disease and colorectal cancer	Store in a cool, dry environment to minimise risk of aflatoxins and salmonella

Food	Vitamins, minerals and phytonutrients	Potential benefits	Precautions
Pears *See pages: 48, 55, 60, 63, 80, 92, 123, 139, 150, 153, 157, 162, 169, 178, 218, 229, 230*	Calcium, carotenoids, fibre, flavonols, folate, iron, magnesium, riboflavin, potassium, vitamins B6, C, K	May assist weight loss; may reduce risk of cancer, hypertension, diabetes and heart disease; treats diverticulosis; lowers levels of constipation, toxins, blood pressure and cholesterol	May increase gas, bloating, pain and diarrhoea in those suffering from irritable bowel disorders
Persimmon  *See pages: 154, 166, 225*	Beta-carotene, beta-cryptoxanthin, betulinic acid, calcium, catechins, choline, copper, fibre, folates, gallocatechins, iron, lutein and zeaxanthin, lycopene, magnesium, manganese, niacin, phosphorus, potassium, pyridoxine, riboflavin, sodium, thiamin, zinc, vitamins A, C, E, K	May be anti-infective, anti-inflammatory and anti-haemorrhagic; helps to prevent age-related macular degeneration	Allergic reaction (very rare)
Pineapple  *See pages: 68, 84, 112, 123, 157, 158, 202*	Beta-carotene, bromelain, calcium, fibre, folate, iron, magnesium, manganese, pantothenic acid, potassium, riboflavin, thiamin, vitamins A, B6, C	May alleviate joint pain, arthritis, inflammation; may inhibit tumour growth and shorten recovery time following plastic surgery; decreases risk and progression of age-related macular degeneration and muscle loss; helps to prevent asthma and kidney stones, to lower blood pressure, and to control blood glucose levels in diabetics; aids digestion, and skin and heart health	Sufferers of gastroesophageal reflux disease may experience heartburn if overconsumed; if taking beta-blockers or your kidneys aren't fully functional, consume in moderation
Pumpkin  *See pages: 165, 173, 209*	Beta-carotene, copper, fibre, folate, iron, magnesium, manganese, niacin, pantothenic acid, phosphorus, potassium, riboflavin, thiamin, vitamins A, B6, C, E	May reduce risk of some cancers, strokes, kidney stones, asthma and heart disease; reduces blood pressure and muscle loss; decreases risk of age-related macular degeneration; boosts fertility and immunity	

Food	Vitamins, minerals and phytonutrients	Potential benefits	Precautions
Radishes *See page: 131*	Beta-carotene, calcium, copper, fibre, folate, iron, lutein and zeaxanthin, magnesium, manganese, niacin, omega-3s, omega-6s, potassium, pyridoxine, riboflavin, sodium, zinc, vitamins A, C, K	May help to combat jaundice, piles, urinary disorders, insect bites, fever, allergies, colds and kidney diseases; decreases risk of some cancers and skin problems; regulates metabolism and functions of liver and gallbladder	May contain goitrogens, which may cause swelling of thyroid in persons with thyroid dysfunction
Raisins  *See page: 189*	Boron, calcium, copper, fibre, folate, iron, magnesium, manganese, niacin, oleanolic acid, pantothenic acid, phosphorus, potassium, pyridoxine, riboflavin, selenium, sodium, thiamin, zinc, vitamins C, E, K	May help to prevent constipation, weight gain, some forms of cancer, sexual dysfunction and hypertension; can help to manage acidosis and anaemia; fights viral and bacterial infections; helps to protect eyes, bones, and teeth; aids bile secretion, lowers cholesterol, and detoxifies body	High calorie content: consume in moderation
Red bell peppers *See page: 76*	Alpha-carotene, beta-carotene, cinnamic acid, cryptoxanthin, ferulic acid, fibre, folate, hesperidin, lutein and zeaxanthin, luteolin, magnesium, manganese, molybdenum, pantothenic acid, phosphorus, potassium, quercetin, vitamins A, B1, B2, B3, B6, C, E, K	May help to prevent cardiovascular disease, age-related macular degeneration and type 2 diabetes; may have potential anti-cancer properties	
Rocket  *See page: 185*	Alpha-lipoic acid, beta-carotene, calcium, copper, fibre, folate, iron, lutein and zeaxanthin, magnesium, manganese, niacin, pantothenic acid, phosphorus, potassium, pyridoxine, riboflavin, selenium, sodium, thiamin, zinc, vitamins A, C, E, K	Lowers blood pressure, reduces oxygen requirement during exercise and enhances athletic performance; may delay or impede cancer; blocks carcinogenic effects of heterocyclic amines; maintains healthy bones; may aid blood glucose control in diabetics	If taking blood-thinners, don't dramatically change level of vitamin K consumption; if improperly stored, nitrates may be converted to nitrites, which can be harmful; take care if using nitrite medications

Food	Vitamins, minerals and phytonutrients	Potential benefits	Precautions
Spinach  *See pages: 48, 51, 52, 56, 64, 67, 71, 72, 75, 76, 79, 80, 84, 87, 103, 107, 112, 116, 136, 158, 166, 169, 170, 177, 178, 181, 182, 185, 186, 222, 229, 230*	Beta-carotene, calcium, copper, fibre, folate, iron, lutein and zeaxanthin, magnesium, manganese, niacin, pantothenic acid, phosphorus, potassium, pyridoxine, riboflavin, sodium, thiamin, zinc, vitamins A, C, E, K	Helps to maintain healthy skin, hair and bones; improves blood glucose control in diabetics; lowers blood pressure, risk of asthma and risk of cancer; aids digestion	If taking beta-blockers or your kidneys aren't fully functional, consume in moderation; if taking blood-thinners, don't dramatically change level of vitamin K consumption
Strawberries  *See pages: 88, 128, 177, 193, 197, 214*	Anthocyanins, calcium, ellagic acid, fibre, folate, iron, kaempferol, magnesium, phosphorus, potassium, quercetin, selenium, vitamins A, C	Reduces inflammation, blood pressure, constipation and risk of some cancers, stroke and heart disease; may help to alleviate symptoms of allergies; aids blood glucose control in diabetics; beneficial for pregnant mothers and those suffering from depression	May be treated with pesticides; if taking beta-blockers or your kidneys aren't fully functional, consume in moderation
Sweet melon (cantaloupe)  *See pages: 103, 143, 201*	Beta-carotene, calcium, choline, fibre, folate, iron, magnesium, niacin, potassium, zeaxanthin, vitamins A, B6, C, K	May help to reduce risk of age-related macular degeneration, asthma and some cancers; decreases blood pressure, inflammation and constipation; helps to maintain healthy skin and hair; promotes healthy sleep, muscle movement, learning and memory	Wash before slicing; if taking beta-blockers or your kidneys aren't fully functional, consume in moderation
Sweet potatoes  *See pages: 64, 99, 136, 182*	Beta-carotene, calcium, fibre, folate, iron, magnesium, manganese, pantothenic acid, phosphorus, potassium, quercetin, riboflavin, thiamin, zinc, vitamins A, B6, C, E	May help to manage blood pressure and blood glucose levels in diabetics; may reduce risk of some cancers; helps to prevent inflammation and constipation, promote fertility and boost immunity; prevents degenerative damage to vision	If taking beta-blockers or your kidneys aren't fully functional, consume in moderation

Food	Vitamins, minerals and phytonutrients	Potential benefits	Precautions
Swiss chard See pages: 48, 140, 144	Alpha-carotene, beta-carotene, calcium, choline, copper, fibre, folate, iron, lutein and zeaxanthin, magnesium, manganese, niacin, pantothenic acid, phosphorus, potassium, pyridoxine, riboflavin, selenium, sodium, thiamin, zinc, vitamins A, C, E, K	Reduces blood pressure, inhibits platelet aggregation and preserves or improves endothelial dysfunction; helps to reduce the risk of cancer and manage diabetes; helps to prevent osteoporosis; improves athletic performance	If taking blood-thinners, don't dramatically change level of vitamin K consumption
Tofu See pages: 210, 222, 226	Calcium, choline, folate, genistein, iron, magnesium, manganese, niacin, phosphorus, riboflavin, selenium, thiamin, vitamins B6, K	May help to reduce risk of cardiovascular disease, breast and prostate cancers, osteoporosis, liver damage and age-related brain diseases; reduces protein excretion in sufferers of type 2 diabetes; can decrease recurrence of breast cancer	Use tofu that has undergone minimal processing
Watermelon See page: 193	Betaine, calcium, choline, copper, fibre, folate, iron, riboflavin, L-citrulline, lycopene, magnesium, manganese, niacin, pantothenic acid, phosphorus, potassium, selenium, sodium, thiamin, zinc, vitamins A, B6, C	Reduces blood pressure and inflammation; lowers risk of asthma and some cancers; hydrates and promotes good digestion, sleep, muscle movement, learning and memory; reduces muscle soreness; maintains healthy skin and hair	
Yoghurt  See pages: 149, 150, 153, 154, 157, 158, 161, 162, 166, 177, 185, 189, 190, 193, 197, 201, 206, 210, 213, 214, 217, 230	Calcium, magnesium, potassium, vitamins B2, B12	Yoghurt with active cultures may counteract lactose intolerance, constipation, diarrhoea, colon cancer, inflammatory bowel disease and *H. pylori* infection; boost the immune system; discourage vaginal infections; prevent osteoporosis; and reduce risk of high blood pressure	

Sources for all the above information are referenced in the section on Ingredients, pages 14-41

Disclaimer: The information in this table has been compiled from several online sources, and is no substitute for an expert medical opinion. Please consult your regular medical practitioner for advice before making any major dietary changes or relinquishing any medication. Neither the author nor the publishers will be held responsible for any resulting ill effects.